EAT
SAFELY

JANET WRIGHT

ORION

An Orion Paperback
First published in Great Britain in 1998 by
Orion Books Ltd,
Orion House, 5 Upper St Martin's Lane,
London WC2H 9EA

A CIP catalogue record for this book
is available from the British Library.

ISBN: 0 75281 544 X

Printed and bound in Great Britain by
The Guernsey Press, Guernsey, C.I.

In memory of my mother, who proved that everyday cooking could be inspired, and Dad who added perfect Yorkshire puddings. For Patricia Hopper, Susan Maysey, Debbie Allen and everyone who's striving to put good food on the table despite the current hazards.

CONTENTS

CHAPTER ONE

What's got into our food?

Why are we suddenly so suspicious about food? It's never been cheaper; we have more products on our shelves than ever before, yet it seems as if every time you open a newspaper there's another food scare.

First we're warned to peel carrots and apples because they're overloaded with pesticides, then we're told to boil our tap water. One minute there's an outbreak of fatal food poisoning, the next it's contaminated baby milk. And the scares about meat are enough to turn anyone vegetarian. We read about new diseases spread by food and wonder what's going on.

Let's be fair, though. Eating has always carried some risks, and we're probably safer today than in previous centuries. Before refrigeration existed, meat went rotten very quickly but people couldn't afford to throw it away. City dwellers might never see fresh food from one season to the next. A mould that grew on wheat caused outbreaks of fatal nerve poisoning. For nineteenth-century Londoners, gin was cheaper than clean water (and much easier to find) – no wonder thousands of them died in cholera epidemics. The major food risk most people faced was starvation.

For nineteenth-century Londoners, gin was cheaper than clean water (and much easier to find)

These days, few people in this part of the world go hungry. Modern production techniques have given us cheap and plentiful food at all times of the year. We've chased away many of the old diseases, especially those carried by rotting food or an unsafe water supply. Even now, we can avoid most food hazards through canny shopping and kitchen-safety techniques.

So we can thank technology for giving us clean water and plenty of food. The trouble is, it didn't stop there. An endless demand for new products – always available and cheap – has led the food industry into strange new areas.

We never thought to question the way our food was being produced till we saw bizarre scenes on television of cattle falling down like drunks. We started learning strange words like bovine spongiform encephalopathy (BSE, or Mad Cow Disease) and Creuzfeldt-Jakob Disease (CJD). Even stranger, we discovered that our own government had abolished the health and safety regulations that were made to protect us.

We couldn't believe it when we first discovered that cows, who naturally live on grass, were being fed the minced-up remnants of diseased sheep – and then fed to us. We heard politicians promising that eating the sick cattle couldn't harm us. Then healthy young people started collapsing with strange and frightening symptoms that finally killed them. Even vegetarians were succumbing as we discovered that the new-variant CJD, the human form of BSE, could lie dormant for many years before starting its deadly work.

The worst of it was the sense that a monster – created not by mad scientists but by penny pinching and low standards – had escaped and couldn't be locked up again. We're not even sure that BSE can't be spread through dairy products. And we've no idea how many years we could be unknowingly harbouring the disease.

Mad Cow Disease isn't the only scare that's drawn our attention to the way our food is produced. The rate of food poisoning in Britain increases year by year: from 14,253 known cases in 1982 (when the present way of calculating figures was introduced) to 83,233 in 1996. The World Health Organisation warns about new strains of old food-borne illnesses like salmonella, Escherichia coli (E coli) and listeria appearing – some of them brought here by imported food. In Britain, modern production methods use massive quantities of drugs and chemicals to provide us with cheap food, but we're starting to question whether all the residues we swallow are doing us any good.

Is it unfair to want the benefits of modern food production without the downside? Perhaps we've just got past the stage of being grateful for having enough to eat, readily available all year round. We've never had to fear cholera from the water, or famine because the crops failed, and we want the future to hold more good things – not new health hazards. As more of us travel abroad and enjoy food picked up in foreign markets, we're also asking why the food we eat here is so bland and tasteless: the same production methods that compromise food safety contribute to its low quality. We're starting to question the price we pay for well-stocked supermarket shelves.

Food hazards fall into two groups. One is mainly connected with food poisoning, in its various forms. There's quite a lot of it about, some stemming from our own kitchens. Luckily that's the easiest to avoid, once you know how to keep and cook food safely. Food can also become contaminated while it's being produced or transported, but that can be avoided when you know what to look out for.

The other main hazard is harder to deal with. It stems from new products and processes that haven't been properly tested – in fact they're being tested now on us, the consumers. Things like irradiation, genetic modification, chemicals on our crops and drugs in the animals we're going to eat. All of these are as tried and tested as … as the new processes that caused BSE. They may prove to be totally harmless, but at present nothing's been proved, and they're already in the foods we eat.

This invisible risk is much harder to quantify. There are few facts and figures, no statistics and little definite information about potential dangers. If you don't want to be a guinea pig, it's harder to avoid these. But it still can be done.

Perhaps, in a roundabout way, BSE did us some good by bringing to our attention the way in which our food is produced. Previously we trusted our farmers and government to do the right thing, without really thinking much about it. Then, when we started asking how farmers were ever allowed to feed cattle with diseased sheep, we discovered a lot of other nasty facts. The overcrowded and insanitary conditions livestock are kept in, for example. The drugs they're given, not to treat illness but as a cheaper way to prevent the diseases caused by their living conditions. The chemicals that were created as weapons but are now used on our food. The cheery abandon with which health and hygiene regulations have been scrapped. The weird new processes tried out on us via our food supply, including science-fiction experiments of swapping plant and animal genes.

Never again will we be so innocently trusting. BSE, it seems, was just the most visible of the monsters created by the food industry. Now we want to make sure the others don't escape to terrorise us. And for that, we have to make it clear to the government, to food manufacturers and to the supermarkets they supply, that we want safe food. We want it produced in sanitary conditions, without the use of unnecessary drugs or chemicals that have not been proved harmless. We don't just want things that look right – we want to be sure they really are clean and safe.

It's annoying, to say the least, when we're warned that some of our favourite foods, like meringues, mayonnaise and home-made ice-cream, are dangerous because they contain uncooked or only lightly cooked eggs. There's nothing harmful about eggs in themselves. The problem here and now is that so many British eggs are contaminated with salmonella or campylobacter. And it's too bad if we like our meat rare, since that is now no longer safe. Why should we give up food made the way we enjoy so that suppliers can go on selling contaminated products?

We have also been shocked by the secrecy surrounding food safety. When a government study in 1996 revealed that fifteen brands of baby milk were contaminated with chemicals, the government refused to say which brands these were. And we no longer accept government assurances that everything's going to be all right. After years of being told BSE couldn't affect human beings, while the evidence mounted that it could and did, we'd like to be treated with a little more respect.

It's not all bad news, though. Pressure groups have made a lot of difference by campaigning for improvements to food safety. Partly as a result of pressure from ordinary people like them, the government has taken a step in the right direction by setting up a new food standards agency. One of the problems has always been that the Ministry of Agriculture, Fisheries and Food (MAFF) had two conflicting roles. It was meant to represent the interests of consumers as well as those of the farmers, supermarket chains and food manufacturers (which are often part of multinational companies with budgets bigger than those of some small countries).

As food campaigners kept pointing out, MAFF could not carry out both its functions fairly when they came into conflict with each other. And we, the consumers, were the weaker partner. It's not just a question of the government endlessly favouring the food industry when we could have done with a little protection from its scary innovations. Time after time, the British government has also tried to prevent EC legislation being passed to benefit the consumer. It has opposed laws that would give us more information: for example, labels on the front of products having to state if they contain artificial sweeteners, a measure which was adopted despite UK opposition. It has refused to support European efforts to restrict the use of unnecessary new drugs, like genetically engineered hormones that would increase a cow's already prodigious milk yield.

But the huge outcry over food scandals like BSE may have shown that we're no longer willing to put up and shut up. It remains to be seen whether the new Food Standards Agency will have the power to override the influence of the food industry and put our interests first.

Meanwhile, we have to be realistic about the risks we face. Food isn't our enemy, and not many of us are likely to die of food poisoning or CJD. In fact, our biggest dietary danger is everyday unhealthy eating habits: too much junk food and saturated fat, not enough fresh fruit or veg. These cause far more illness – serious stuff like heart disease and cancer – than any bacteria, only it's not sudden and dramatic. It's true we can't yet guess how many people will die from eating BSE-infected burgers, since we don't know how long it takes for the symptoms to develop. Judging from present knowledge, however, if anything strikes us down, it's more likely to be that not-quite-defrosted chicken breast that we cooked for a quick lunch. We can still ask the farmers to stop selling dangerous meat. Meanwhile, importantly, we can protect ourselves by storing and cooking it the right way.

Anyone reading a book like this probably knows what to look for in the shops and keeps their kitchen clean already. But it's quite surprising how many small details make a difference. You're careful about reheating meat, but would you take the same precautions with rice? Why does it matter if ham and bacon are kept side by side in the supermarket – or in your fridge? How can you avoid products containing genetically modified ingredients, since this information isn't on the label? Do you actually know how cold your fridge is? And would you say no to ice-and-lemon in your holiday drink?

Read on to find out how to reduce the risks and be sure you and your family are eating safely.

DARE I EAT ANYTHING?

When you start looking into food safety it seems as if practically everything's got a question mark hanging over it. You hardly dare put anything in your mouth – if it didn't cause food poisoning or fatal illness, it could be laden with chemicals, or storing up cancer for the future.

Luckily that's not really the case. True, we can't weigh up all the risks because we don't know what some of them are, like what pesticide residues do to us in the long term, but the risks we know most about are quite easily sidestepped. Food poisoning is on the rise, but that's the easiest to prevent ourselves: simple things like putting food in a different part of the fridge, or shopping on the way home from work instead of in the lunch hour, make most of the difference.

Seeing a whole book devoted to eating safely is quite unnerving – are there really so many rules to follow? No, it's not that complicated. It's more about showing what's really important and finding the easiest ways to do it. Eating safely isn't about trying to create unrealistically sterile conditions – after all, you're never likely to have to do emergency brain surgery on your kitchen floor. Germs and human beings have existed side by side since the world began. If you get too obsessed with them you end up like poor millionaire Howard Hughes: never daring to leave his home and eating only out of tins because he thought nothing else was safe. There's just no need to give the germs an unfair advantage.

As for the hazards that haven't existed since time began – things like chemical pesticides, irradiation, genetic engineering – the safest answer is to try to minimise the risks. This means simply avoiding them till we know whether they're safe or not.

CHAPTER TWO

Safe shopping

Short of digging up our back gardens and growing everything ourselves, we can't guarantee the quality of the food we eat. But we can side-step a lot of the risks by careful shopping.

Keep fragile food undamaged and frozen food frozen

For a start, we can keep fragile food undamaged and frozen food frozen by picking them up in the right order. Supermarkets put the fresh fruit and vegetables near the entrance to entice shoppers in. Do they think we'd change our mind about shopping if we couldn't see the carrots from the door? You don't have to follow their layout – it's a better idea to go round in this order: bleach and chemicals first, in a corner of the trolley where they don't come in contact with untinned food. Then tins and packets, all the non-perishables. Then fresh fruit and veg, placed on top of everything else. Next stop: items from the chilled cabinets, and finally those from the freezer. Make some space in the trolley to pack all the cold foods in together, to keep them cool, then head straight for the check-out so they have as little chance as possible to thaw out.

As you go along the shelves, check the use-by or best-before dates. Are the latest ones at the back? Those are the ones you want. No need to ignore goods in the bargain bin, though: if they're still in date but just about to expire, buy them to eat that day. If they're past their best-before date, the contents may not be as crisp or fresh as you'd like, though they should still be safe.

While you're there, cheap damaged tins or packets are tempting when money's tight. But they're a false economy. Any damage may have allowed germs into the tin – even if it's just dented or rusty – and if it's bulging the food inside is inedible anyway. Point this out to the manager, since food from damaged tins can cause a deadly form of food poisoning called botulism. A torn packet is no longer safe for use, either. And if anything in a non-refrigerated bargain bin would normally be kept in the fridge, don't take the risk.

Fruit and veg come after you've put all the heavy stuff in your trolley, so they don't get squashed when everything else lands on top of them. That's not just a nuisance: bacteria can breed under the broken skin. When you reach the fresh fruit and veg, look out for locally grown produce, preferably in season. Out-of-season fruit and veg will have been encouraged with even more fertiliser than those that are growing at their natural time. Exotic produce flown in from far afield is more likely to be contaminated by chemicals that have been banned over here and by bacteria picked up along the way. Our food now comes from all around the world, bringing new bugs with it. Recent outbreaks of dysentery in Britain and Scandinavia, for example, were traced to contaminated lettuce imported from southern Europe.

Wherever they come from, fruit and vegetables should look fresh and undamaged. Leaves should be crisp, root vegetables firm, skin unbroken. That doesn't mean they have to be perfectly round and identical in size. Organic food is famous for its funny knobbly shapes and inconvenient sizes – we've almost forgotten that's the way things naturally grow. But you don't want anything that's on the verge of going off. The older or more damaged it is, the worse it will taste and the less good it will do you anyway.

Ready-prepared salad and vegetables are tempting when you're in a hurry (and who isn't?) but look closely before you pick them up. Is there any hint of brownness where they've been cut? Do they look slightly limp or wilted? This kind of partly prepared food has already lost some of its vitamins and may be less fresh than produce that hasn't been cut. You're also paying an awful lot for someone to tear up lettuce leaves or chop green beans for you, but to be realistic, buying this is better than rushing straight past the fresh fruit and veg because you're not going to have time to prepare it.

When you reach the deli counter, carefully avoid any cooked items that could have touched raw meat or seafood. The bacteria in raw meat are destroyed by cooking, but if they transfer on to precooked items they'll survive into your stomach. In fact, if a shop is careless enough to display food like this, be suspicious of its other hygiene practices.

When you reach the fridges, look for latest sell-by dates and pass over items at the front that may have been warmed up by handling. On your last stop before the check-out, dig deep into the bottom of the freezer to take out the coldest foods. Pack all frozen goods into bags together, so they can help keep each other cold, then get home as quickly as possible. If you have to shop during your lunch hour, make sure there's room in the freezer compartment of your workplace fridge – unless it's so cold outside that the bag of frozen food would stay frosted on the window ledge. Otherwise, buy freezer goods on the way home from work. An insulated bag is a really good buy, especially for meat and dairy products. Just one hour in a carrier bag is enough to allow bacteria to start breeding, and it happens even faster on a hot day. If frozen food has started thawing by the time you get home, don't refreeze it. Put it in the fridge and use it within the next few days.

IMPORTANT POINTS

- Don't buy damaged tins or packets.
- Get frozen food home before it has time to start defrosting.
- Check sell-by and best-before dates.

LABELS

More than half of us admit in surveys that we don't read food labels. Maybe it wouldn't matter if we could feel perfectly confident of what we were buying, but the deregulation of the food industry over the past few years means that there's no longer such tight control over what can be put in our food. That makes reading the labels more important than ever. When the Consumers' Association tested seventy supermarket products, it found that less than one in ten contained exactly the amount of nutrients stated on the label. Nearly half the labels were out by more than ten per cent. And that's not the only aspect that can be misleading to the safety-conscious shopper.

> **The use-by date on a food is the latest time it can be guaranteed safe to eat**

The use-by date on a food is the latest time it can be guaranteed safe to eat; after that you're taking a risk. The sell-by date usually gives you a few days' leeway. It's an offence for shops to sell food after the use-by or sell-by date. Best-before labels, on items like tinned food that don't deteriorate so quickly, are about quality rather than safety. You should still be able to eat the food safely for a while after the best-before date, but it may not be so fresh or tasty.

The ingredients in a product have to be listed in descending order of weight, so the first item is whatever there is the most of in the package. So, if you're trying to cut down on sugar, look out for all its other names. A product that seems to be low in sugar may have several helpings of it under various names. The word 'sugar' actually covers several different substances: the real name of the white sprinkly stuff is 'sucrose', for example; then there are glucose, fructose, lactose and maltose, all of them forms of sugar. Look out for words like 'syrup', also a form of sugar, and maltodextrin, which is a corn-starch product that's midway between starch and sugar.

Be wary of products claiming to have 'reduced fat', 'less sugar' or 'extra fibre'. More or less than what? When people like the Food Commission or the Consumers' Association do reports on this kind of product, they report funny examples of one manufacturer's 'low-fat' product having more fat than another's standard version, or one product having half the calories of another because it's little more than half the size! It makes a good read, but it's annoying when you're trying to compare products in a crowded supermarket with ten minutes to go before closing time.

'Low sugar' often means lots of artificial sweetener instead. Though sugar rots your teeth, artificial sweeteners have been linked with a range of unhealthy side effects. They're among

> *'Low sugar' often means lots of artificial sweetener instead*

the many additives it's worth trying to cut down on.

Many of us look out for E-numbers as a guide to how many additives a product contains. All E-numbers have been cleared for use in Europe and foods officially contain too little of them to do any harm. Some are worth adding: E300, for example, is good old vitamin C, and some are preservatives, which, like it or not, are necessary when food's being packaged for a long shelf life. Food-safety campaigners, however, say there are question marks over many of them.

Realising people were suspicious of E-numbers, some manufacturers have taken to putting the full name instead. They figure that words like tartrazine (E102, a yellow colouring linked with hyperactivity), amaranth or erythrosine (the red colourings E123 and E127, possibly carcinogenic) don't have the same unwholesome reputation. The list of suspects is too long to print here. But look out for any heavily processed foods, especially if they're brightly coloured, highly flavoured or very sweet.

IMPORTANT E POINTS

- The more processed a food is, the more likely it is to contain dubious additives. Gaudy colours and unnatural tastes are a clue.
- E-numbers that have been linked with some kind of health risk (though these may not all have been

conclusively proven) are E102, E110, E122–E124, E127, E129, E131, E133, E142, E150c, E151, E153, E154, E155, E210–E224, E226–E228, E232, E249–E252, E284, E285, E320, E321, E512, E553b, E621, E942, E954, E1440.

EGGS

Words like 'farm fresh' and other cheery rural descriptions on egg boxes sound like the kind of thing you'd like to buy. In reality, they mean these are battery eggs. These eggs were laid in huge factory farms where hens spend their entire lives crammed into cages 18 inches high with no room to stretch or move freely. In Britain, eighty-five per cent of all our eggs are produced in this way, yet few supermarkets are open about this: the Co-op is unusual in labelling these honestly as 'intensively produced'. The terms 'barn' and 'perchery' eggs cover a multitude of conditions, some not much better than batteries. Hens aren't caged and have the freedom to fly on to perches, but are still kept in heavily crowded barns.

When we read the words 'free-range eggs' most of us think of chickens pecking happily and healthily around the farmyard, eating natural food. As the Soil Association discovered when it tried to prise information out of the supermarkets, free range chickens do have to be given access to the open air but they can be crowded inside barns for up to sixteen hours a day, with as many as 7000 in one barn. They may also be fed on the same drugs and foods as battery hens, including animal protein, which is believed to be a way for diseases to jump the species barrier – like Mad Cow Disease.

Organic eggs are safest and are produced in the best conditions. In supermarkets, if there's no organic food, the thing to look for is the RSPCA's Freedom Food label. This has disappointed some people, since it permits debeaking and routine medication, for example, but it sets the highest generally available standard.

Organic and Freedom Food eggs are produced in better conditions,so they're likely to come from healthier hens. But no eggs are guaranteed free of infection, so you should still take the same precautions, which is not eating them raw or lightly cooked if you're unwell or pregnant.

Look for the RSPCA's Freedom Food label

IMPORTANT POINTS

- Open egg cartons before you buy, to check that they're not dirty, since dirt can seep through the shells, or cracked. Cracked eggs aren't just a messy nuisance; the eggs are open to infection.
- If there's any fuzzy growth on the shells they may be mouldy, and a smell like hay could mean bacterial infection.
- Hold the egg up to the light if you're at all suspicious. The contents should be clear with a small air sac (less than 6mm deep). Turn the egg slightly to see that the yolk doesn't rotate much.
- Look out for the best-before date: with eggs this really is a use-by date.

MEAT

Meat is the basis of our national cuisine – who can imagine a roast dinner without it? – but in its various forms it's the biggest headache for anyone concerned with food safety. Meat is the major cause of food poisoning, whether at home or eating out. It's reached the crazy point where, early in 1998, the British Medical Association warned that all raw meat should be treated as if it's infected with harmful bacteria: to avoid food poisoning, you need to be very careful about storage and cooking.

Meat carries frightening new diseases and, thanks to overuse of antibiotics on farm animals, can end up making our medicines ineffective. Most disturbingly, we don't really know for sure what is safe from diseases like BSE which are caused by new food-production techniques.

When shopping for meat, plain cuts are usually a better choice than ready-made mixed-meat products like sausages, pies or burgers. The risk of BSE is supposed to be low, now that all older cattle have been destroyed

> *Plain cuts are usually a better choice than ready-made mixed-meat products*

– we're told that the young animals we now eat are safe. But advice keeps changing as new scientific evidence appears. And another fatal brain disease, called idiopathic brainstem neuronal chromatolysis, has been found in British cattle, mainly affecting beef herds. Though the government says it can't spread to humans, that's just what it used to say about BSE (see The Mad Cow Story, page 115).

BSE was originally found in the brains and spinal cords of cattle, so some people believe the more expensive cuts of meat – from muscle only – are safer, although these could still have come in contact with the contaminated parts at the abattoir. Some people believe the nerves contained in muscles might also carry the disease, but it was things like sausages, pies and burgers, with all kinds of animal bits minced in together, that were thought most likely to carry BSE.

The trouble is, the word 'meat' can cover practically any part of the animal, including hooves, gristle – you name it. That goes for any kind of meat, not just beef. Tasty though they may be, cheap products are made with the lowest-quality meat that often contains a kind of sludge, called 'mechanically recovered meat', which includes the bits you'd rather bin.

If you're buying mince, choose some meat at the butcher's and ask for it to be minced for you – any good butcher will do this. Ready-minced meat tends to be lower quality and high in fat – not a real bargain anyway, as it shrinks away in the frying pan.

Many shoppers swapped from beef to chicken after the BSE scare. But the Consumers' Association recently found that a third of the chickens its testers bought from major supermarket chains were unfit for human consumption. The words 'free range', once used for traditionally reared chickens, now has a more restricted meaning. Only poultry labelled as 'free range total freedom' has unrestricted access to the outdoors, but even these may be routinely fed with antibiotics and other drugs.

The bacterium E. coli, which caused a fatal outbreak of food poisoning in Lanarkshire, Scotland in 1996 that killed eighteen people and affected 272 others, has been found for the first time in lamb and in venison. It's quite common in beef already – one study found it in twenty-two per cent of raw beef products tested. Luckily, like most bacteria, it's killed by thorough cooking at a high temperature.

Modern farming methods mean that most of the meat we buy comes from animals that have been dosed on drugs, including antibiotics – not to cure diseases but as a routine measure to prevent them. This meat sometimes contains drug residues and because this has only started happening in the past few decades, we don't really know the long-term effects. Although liver is a good health choice, being full of the iron our bodies need, it's also the part of the animal that's most likely to contain drug or chemical residues.

The Consumers' Association has found antibiotic residues in turkey and pork – worrying evidence that these over-used drugs are getting through to us. Though doctors give us antibiotics only to cure an infection, farmers routinely dose their animals with these powerful drugs as a preventive measure. Antibiotics can even be used to make the animals grow faster.

The trouble is, over-use of antibiotics creates new strains of 'superbugs' that are resistant to them. And that leads to diseases – among people as well as animals – that can no longer be cured by antibiotics. This frightening scenario is already well known in hospitals. In fact, food poisoning outbreaks have become more dangerous now that bacteria are resistant to the antibiotics that used to wipe them out.

Organic meat is the safest option (see page 122) but it's not widely available yet in supermarkets, so look out for schemes which go some way towards raising standards, such as RSPCA Freedom Food, Sainsbury's Partnership in Livestock or Tesco's Nature's Choice.

IMPORTANT POINTS

- Shop somewhere that's clean and busy, with a quick turnover of food which is kept in cool enough conditions by staff who don't touch it with their bare hands.
- Check that raw and cooked products don't come in contact with each other – staff should even use different utensils to pick them up.
- Make sure each piece of meat is wrapped separately.
- Choose simple cuts of meat rather than products made with mixed meat, which are at greater risk of cross-contamination. Also, formed meat products, like turkey roll, are hard to cook thoroughly without drying out.
- Avoid ready-to-eat chicken that doesn't need reheating. It has caused too many cases of food poisoning to be worth the risk.
- When buying raw meat, check that it looks firm and fresh and is a healthy pink colour.
- Don't forget there are animal by-products in many seemingly vegetarian foods: lard in vegetable pies, for example, and gelatine in vitamin capsules. Read all labels!

FISH

Fish used to seem like the safe answer to concerns about meat. After all, they swim freely in the sea, far from farmers wielding drugs and chemicals, don't they? The trouble is, the sea isn't the cleanest place to be any more. The marine pollution that hits the headlines when it kills lovable seals or dolphins has a steady long-term effect on our food supplies too.

Our own North Sea is very heavily polluted, with industrial waste, with sewage from ships and with farm chemicals that have run off into rivers. Pesticides including DDT and dieldrin have been found in both farmed and sea-caught fish. The Ministry of Agriculture, Fisheries and Food is investigating the problem. In one investigation, a third of the fish were found to have skin diseases and strange growths. What should we do? One answer is to get to know your local fishmonger and ask for fish that's not caught in the North Sea. Alternatively, buy frozen – if it's frozen, it could be brought in from anywhere, reducing the chance it was caught in our polluted local waters.

There's no definite evidence that these deformed fish are harmful to us, though, and fish is still a very healthy food. Most of the poisons go into the liver, so a fillet should be quite safe.

Farmed fish, of course, run the same risks as farmed animals. Salmon, once a rare treat, is now one of our favourite buys. Most of the salmon we eat is intensively farmed, meaning the fish live their lives in huge aquatic cages. Their food includes dyes to give their greyish skin a cheerful pink tone, and with little space to move around, their bodies contain more fat, though not necessarily as much of the healthy essential fatty acids we're recommended to eat.

> *Farmed fish, of course, run the same risks as farmed animals*

The unnaturally crowded conditions put farmed salmon at

risk of infections and infes-
tations. In fact, a parasite
called the sea louse is now
so widespread that it poses
a danger to the whole industry. The latest solution is a
poison called Ivermectin
that kills lice by paralysing

> *Wild salmon may cost more, but the taste makes it a treat worth waiting for*

their nervous system. The worry about that, of course, is that it
might possibly affect people eating the fish. Some supermarkets won't stock fish that have been treated with Ivermectin.
But if we want cheap salmon, which means crowded intensive
farming, how else can the producers destroy the lice?

Luckily, we don't have to think of a solution. Wild salmon may
cost more, but the taste makes it a treat worth waiting for. You
should be able to spot it by its more delicate, natural pink colouring.
You'll often find wild Pacific salmon quite cheaply in tins.

IMPORTANT POINTS

- When buying fresh fish, look for clear eyes, red gills, shiny skin
  and scales still in place. The fish should feel firm and slightly
  resilient if you press it. Avoid fish with dull eyes and dry or
  slimy skin.
- Don't freeze fresh fish. Eat it the same day it was bought.
- A strong fishy smell means it's past its best. Don't buy it.
- With frozen fish, check that it's frozen hard, with no white
  patches or ice crystals on the flesh, and the seal is unbroken.
  It needs to be in your own freezer within ninety minutes.
- Don't buy ready-to-eat fish (such as smoked salmon or
  kippers) if it's displayed close to raw fish.
- As with meat, buy fish from a clean and busy place with a
  quick turnover.

CHAPTER THREE

Safe in the kitchen

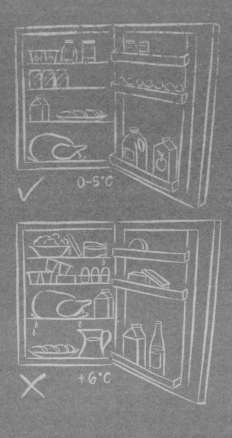

✓ 0-5°C

✗ +6°C

W hen a big food-poisoning outbreak hits the headlines, it's usually caused by a supplier, or the caterer at some big function. In reality most cases of food poisoning happen at home – we don't hear so much about these because no one is prosecuted. And it's on the increase. That's partly because we're sold infected eggs and contaminated cook-chill foods. But it's also partly because we're eating more raw food and using microwave ovens. Our kitchens are warm, too, and we keep food for days or weeks instead of eating it when it's fresh. The pace of modern life means we rarely have time to shop and cook every day. So we have to take extra precautions to keep our food safe.

Food poisoning is most often caused by meat, seafood or eggs. Nearly all British poultry, for example, is bred in crowded batteries where disease spreads fast. The Central Public Health Laboratory warns that more

> *Food poisoning is most often caused by meat, seafood or eggs*

than thirty per cent of chicken carcasses are contaminated with salmonella, seventy-six per cent with campylobacter and a small number with listeria.

Luckily, these bacteria can all be destroyed by thorough heating, so even a contaminated chicken shouldn't do any harm if it's properly cooked. Even so, salmonella is responsible for nearly 30,000 cases of vomiting and diarrhoea a year, including forty to fifty deaths. Campylobacter is even more common, causing 43,240 cases of diarrhoea in 1996. Listeria, though far less common, causes at least ten deaths a year and an unknown number of miscarriages. E. coli poisoning has steadily increased to more than 1000 cases a year, some of them fatal. It can cause kidney failure in children, as well as the more usual vomiting and diarrhoea.

> Even a contaminated chicken shouldn't do any harm if it's properly cooked

But food poisoning isn't the only danger we have to protect ourselves and our families from. The food we eat may have been treated with up to twenty-seven applications of chemicals, many of which have not been proved safe. Several government studies have found higher than acceptable levels of pesticides in food on sale. Though the official line is that these levels are still not harmful, there's no information yet available about the long-term effects, especially of those containing organophosphates.

With those sobering facts in mind, scoot the cat off the kitchen table and make a few home safety checks.

STORAGE

For a start, how cold is your fridge? It's impossible to guess, so you really need a fridge thermometer, preferably fixed inside. Available from hardware shops and department stores, it may give you a surprise. I didn't notice, for example, that someone had turned the fridge temperature down making it too cold, till a can of soft drink at the back turned to ice and exploded. It's not

✓ 0–5°C

✗ +6°C

a question of the colder the better: if the temperature's too cold food will partially freeze. Apart from spoiling the texture, this means it may not thaw out properly when it's cooked. This will prevent the food cooking properly and may allow food-poisoning bacteria to survive.

On the other hand, bacteria thrive in a fridge that's not cold enough. One of the commonest ways of warming up a fridge is by leaving the door open. So get people to take out what they want and shut the door as rapidly as possible. If anyone in the household tends to leave the fridge door open while they pour milk for coffee and Corn Flakes, give them the electricity bill.

Put the thermometer somewhere easy to see, in the coldest part of the fridge. In a larger fridge (one that doesn't have a freezing compartment) this is usually the lowest shelf above the salad crisper; if your fridge is the sort that does have an ice-box, the top and middle shelves of the fridge are probably coldest. A frost-free fridge should be about the same temperature everywhere. Leave the thermometer overnight to settle to the right temperature, then read it without picking it up. The coldest part should be between zero and five degrees C. So adjust the thermostat by turning it down to zero, then to the right setting: the highest number is usually the coldest setting, but check the fridge instructions to be certain. Then leave it overnight again and check that the temperature is right. If you haven't got the fridge instructions, ask in a shop, ring the manufacturers or just keep trying till you get it right.

The Consumers' Association warns that the most accurate thermometers are also the most responsive. This means the reading can change very fast as soon as you open the door, so you need to check it quickly. While you're checking the temperature, make sure the fridge isn't packed too full, which stops cold air circulating properly.

Vital though they are in our centrally heated homes, fridges can give a false sense of security. We tend to think anything in the fridge is kept in suspended animation. In reality, very few foods should be kept longer than about five days. Refrigeration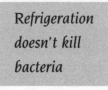

Refrigeration doesn't kill bacteria

doesn't kill bacteria, and the really hardy ones like listeria can even go on breeding in fridges. Most foods have a short fridge life: a couple of days for milk, cream or cooked food; only twelve hours for fish. As long as hard cheese looks all right it probably is.

But don't keep soft cheese for more than a few days, and throw it out at once if it looks discoloured or starts leaking liquid.

Meat has to be kept especially carefully. Uncooked meat needs to be kept a safe distance away from other food, especially if that food is ready to eat. Bacteria from raw meat can easily contaminate the other food, and if it then won't be destroyed by cooking it's a serious food-poisoning risk. All cooked food should be stored at the top of the fridge, with raw meat and seafood separated from everything else at the bottom, where they can't drip on to anything. Any food that was cut from a bulk pack in the shop, such as paté or salami, should be used within forty-eight hours.

> *All cooked food should be stored at the top of the fridge*

Poultry shouldn't be kept more than twenty-four hours in the fridge. If you're not going to cook it within this time, buy a frozen bird and put it in the freezer, leaving plenty of time to defrost it when it's needed. It's not really safe to freeze chicken or other poultry yourself, since these are the likeliest things to carry food-poisoning bugs and if you don't get the temperature quite right they could survive.

Should eggs go in the fridge or not? Food-safety experts used to say no. They advised leaving eggs in a cool place, since they haven't been refrigerated before. Dampness in a fridge could dissolve the shell's protective coating and they risk getting too cold to cook through properly. Now the government recommends putting eggs in the least cold part of the fridge, for example the door, since temperatures outside tend to fluctuate. Either way, don't wash or wipe them.

Most fresh fruit and veg should be kept in the fridge. If anything arrived home bruised, cut out the damaged part and use what's left the same day. The rest of your buy should be stored without being washed or cut up: once it's peeled or cut it starts rapidly losing vitamins and soon goes off. If you bought vegetables in plastic packs, open them up to stop them sweating.

Root vegetables can be kept outside the fridge in a dark airy place. Potatoes should be kept in a paper bag to stop them going green – green potatoes are toxic. Unripe fruit can be left out to ripen, or wrapped in paper and left in a dark place like a drawer (just don't forget it's there).

There are a few fruit and veg that should be kept away from each other. Onions, garlic and leeks are best kept in paper bags, well apart from anything that could pick up an oniony smell. Potatoes go off sooner if they're in contact with onions, and being stored near apples makes carrots taste bitter. Bananas turn black fast in the fridge, and shouldn't be kept with other fruit since they give off a gas that makes the others ripen too fast. This gas could help, though, with those rock-hard peaches and nectarines that never seem to ripen …

When you put cooked leftovers in the fridge, let them cool down first to avoid raising its temperature. That reduces the fridge's effectiveness and encourages the growth of mould – which could get on to food and be harmful – as well as wasting money. Stand food in a bowl of ice water to cool down quickly: ninety minutes is the longest time anything that needs to be refrigerated should stay outside the fridge. Don't keep leftovers of custard, gravy or anything else that has been made up from a powder containing meat, eggs, rice or dairy products. These ingredients are those most likely to harbour food-poisoning bacteria, which start multiplying fast when you add water and warmth. They will usually have been cooked before being dried, so you are already 'reheating' them when you make them up from powder to soup, or granules to gravy.

Food shouldn't stay in a tin once it's been opened, since it can become contaminated by the metal. You can buy specially

> *Ninety minutes is the longest time anything that needs to be refrigerated should stay outside the fridge*

made containers with lids for the fridge, or simply transfer any unused contents to a china mug or bowl and cover it with a saucer. If you use cling film, it's best not to let it touch the food. Cling film should never be put on fatty food such as cheese, or on food that is still hot. There's a possibility that some of the chemicals in cling film may be harmful, but it's thought to be fine as long as it's stretched across the container above cold food. Greaseproof paper is also safe.

Ideally we're meant to defrost the fridge every week, throwing away practically anything that's been there since last time. The young and carefree leave it till the door won't shut, by which time the fridge really isn't working at all and half its contents are lethal. Most of us strike a balance between the two. It needs to be emptied and cleaned with a teaspoonful of bicarbonate of soda – better than detergent, which could taint the food – in a pint (600ml) of hot water, at least every few weeks. This is also when you can throw out all the scraps and food that's passed its use-by date. A dab of vanilla essence on the rinsing cloth makes the fridge smell nice. And there's so much more room when you've been ruthless in throwing out the leftovers. Any spills in the fridge should be mopped up at once.

Though freezing doesn't kill all bacteria, the freezer is a safer place than the fridge. Chest-type freezers are safest of all, since the cold air doesn't fall out when you open them. Those stars on packets of frozen food (one star for a week, two for a month and three for three months) refer to the amount of time food will look and taste its best.

Freezers should stay below minus eighteen degrees C and be packed as full as possible to keep the temperature (and your electricity bills) down. Filling the gaps with bread will help. To make sure the temperature is right, buy a freezer thermometer. Like fridge thermometers, they only cost a few pounds, but instead of putting them in the coldest

> *Freezers should stay below minus eighteen degrees C*

part you put freezer thermometers in the warmest part. This is usually at the top; opposite the hinges in an upright model.

Crafty cooks often make twice as much as they need and freeze half to eat later. An excellent time-saving tip, as long as you have a four-star freezer (one with three stars or less is only suitable for storing already frozen food). Cool the food quickly by putting its container into a bowl full of ice, then put it into freezer bags, each one containing a meal-sized portion. Label them with the date and what it is, since this may not be quite so obvious when it's frozen solid. Fast-freeze them on the coldest setting – two to four hours is long enough to freeze most foods, but a joint of meat may take up to twenty-four hours. Remember to put things in the bottom, or the back, of the freezer so older items get used first.

When you take meat out of the freezer, be especially careful to defrost it properly before cooking – preferably in a drip-proof container at the bottom of the fridge, rather than in a warm room where bacteria could start reproducing. Check in advance how long it's going to take to defrost, so you don't find yourself having to start cooking when it's still frozen in the middle. Microwave defrosting isn't ideal, since it partially cooks the food, but it does enormously cut down on waiting time: a large turkey that would take three days to defrost in the fridge, or two in a cool room, would be ready to cook in less than an hour using the microwave. So if you do use the microwave, just make sure there's no ice left inside. Don't refreeze food that's thawed but has not been cooked.

Freezers need to be defrosted and cleaned, though not so often as fridges. A good time to do this is when supplies are low, since it's important not to refreeze anything that's thawed. It's useful if you and a close neighbour can arrange to use some space in each other's freezer when one of you is defrosting. Otherwise the family can enjoy an unusual dinner comprising everything that needed to be used up.

Ideally, all foods except fresh root vegetables and bananas should be kept either in the fridge or in airtight containers. You can buy plastic storage containers, or just wash and reuse old coffee jars with uncracked lids, throwing out the cardboard that lined the lid. Any clean jar will do, as long as it doesn't smell of the food that was previously in it, but coffee jars are a favourite old standby because you can buy them big enough to empty entire packets into. Airtight containers not only keep the air from spoiling food, but reduce the risk of spillages and insect infestation. Even if they're unopened, packets are a godsend to cockroaches and mice (yes, the nicest homes can have them). Don't refill a container until it is empty and you've washed it out, otherwise the last inch or so of food may stay at the bottom getting stale and unhealthy. Dry the container thoroughly before refilling, so you don't risk the contents going mouldy. If you do find mould on anything, throw it out, as the spores may have permeated all the way through.

Read the label on anything you buy, even if you take it for granted that it doesn't need to go in the fridge. New processes mean more foods need refrigeration these days. We all eat too much sugar, salt and fat, so it's healthy to cut down on these. But they do happen to help preserve food naturally. So 'light' foods that are low in fat, salt, or sugar may need to be stored in the fridge: the label should tell you.

If tins don't carry a date, mark them with the date they were bought. Though tinned food will normally have been sterilised by heat and should last a long time, it won't last for ever. Kept in a cool, dry place and if undamaged, corned beef, salmon and fish in oil will keep for five years, according to the Food Safety Advisory Centre. Tins of peas, beans, pulses and mushrooms will last four years. Other tinned meat and fish will last up to three years, along with sweet corn, carrots, spinach, unpeeled potatoes, pineapple and most deciduous fruits (such as peaches). Tins of tomatoes last two and a half years. Baked beans, peeled potatoes, citrus fruit, soft fruit and apples should be used within two years. Canned ready meals, sauces and soups have a shelf life of one year, while dairy products, rice pudding and fizzy drinks should be used within six months. Always check that the tin is undamaged before you use it, especially along the seal, since the contents of damaged tins can cause botulism. It's also a good idea to wipe the tops of tins before opening them.

When you're cleaning the kitchen shelves (which you don't have to do quite so often if you have everything stored in airtight containers) take the chance to check best-before dates, move older items to the front and make

Check that the tin is undamaged before you use it

sure nothing has become damaged. Slowly tilt containers of powdery food such as flour so you can see it move: if it seems to stick together or there's a cobwebby look, it's been spoilt by damp or insects and needs to be thrown away. Either of these is much more likely if food is left in open packets. It's rare in the English climate, but you do occasionally get tiny insects breeding, even in an airtight container, if their eggs were already in the food before you put it away.

Hold packets up to the light to see if there are any tiny holes – if so, out they go. You don't want to share your food with whatever has been nibbling it. Other evidence of mice or insects includes droppings (sometimes just little black specks like pepper), fragments of food found in odd places and of course tiny footprints in anything that's been spilt. This is one reason to clear up spills as soon as they happen – they're a magnet to all kinds of things from bacteria up. If you see any of these signs, check every item of food that's not in the fridge. Are any containers cracked? Do any lids not fit tightly enough? Throw out anything that wasn't in a safe container, then scrub your shelves and cupboards with bleach and treat yourself to a new set of containers. If it's mice, you'll need to keep soap in a container too.

If the problem persists, ring your local council's Environmental Health Department. From your description, they will be able to tell you what the intruder is and either give you advice or send someone to deal with it. If you use insect killer, follow the instructions carefully. Many of them are dangerous to children and pets and some can trigger asthma attacks. Make sure all food is covered before you use pesticide.

IMPORTANT POINTS

- Most food apart from bananas and some root vegetables should go either in the fridge or in airtight containers. Check the labels to make sure.
- Don't wrap fatty food in cling film.
- Defrost the fridge regularly and keep it clean. Check it's between zero and five degrees C.
- Keep raw meat or seafood covered in a container, and don't let it come into contact with any other food.
- Food won't last for weeks, even in the fridge. The freezer is the only safe place for long-term storage of anything perishable.

DEADLY BLESSINGS

Not many fresh foods will do you any harm, but there are some that shouldn't be eaten, and a few things need special preparation to destroy natural toxins. Red kidney beans and soya beans, for example, need to be boiled for ten minutes to destroy a harmful protein called haemagglutinin, which can cause severe gastroenteritis. Tinned beans are already cooked, so they're safe to eat straight from the can; you don't even need to heat them. But if you're using dried beans soak them overnight first, drain off the water they soaked in, add cold water, then bring them to a rolling boil for ten minutes. If you're slow-cooking a chilli con carne or a bean stew, it's best to boil the beans first.

If you buy fresh rhubarb, throw away the leaves. They contain toxic levels of oxalic acid, which can block the body's absorption of calcium. There's also some in the stalks (and in spinach), but not enough to do any harm unless you have a tendency to form kidney stones. Rhubarb occasionally has a laxative effect.

Throw out any potatoes that have gone green – don't just cut off the green part. They contain a toxin called solanine that can cause stomach upsets and diarrhoea and has been known to kill. It's already present, in smaller amounts, when potatoes start to sprout, so use them up quickly or bin them if you see signs of sprouting.

FOOD PREPARATION

When you're preparing a meal, always use one knife and chopping board for raw meat or seafood and another for all other foods, washing them (not just wiping down) after

> *Always use one knife and chopping board for raw meat or seafood*

each use. It's the only way you can be sure you're not spreading live bacteria from raw food on to anything that isn't going to be cooked. If you had raw meat on a plate in the fridge, wash it up as soon as you take the meat off – don't put the cooked meat or any other food on the unwashed plate.

If you're worried about the bugs that breed around food, kitchen products containing the chlorine compound triclosan, or Microban, sound appealing. But ask yourself whether you really want these colossally powerful chemicals around your food. After all their by-products, dioxins, are notorious pollutants that collect in our bodies as well as in the environment. Your Microban-impregnated ladle may not fill you with dioxins, but it could be helping breed new generations of super-tough bacteria that resist any weaker cleaning agent. By raising the stakes this way – as with the 'preventive' use of antibiotics in healthy animals – we actually make it harder to fight off germs. Anyway, researchers have been surprised to find that good old wooden chopping boards were more germ resistant than the cleaner-looking plastic ones. Maybe Mother Nature knows something they don't?

Cats love jumping on the table to join you, but do put them firmly back on the floor. You shouldn't even stroke pets while you're cooking: you need to wash your hands after you've touched them if you're preparing food. If you can't resist their pleading eyes while you're eating, put a bit of food on one side for them till you've finished, then put it in their own bowls – never let them lick the plates that people use. Pet foods should be kept separate and served with a spoon you don't use for anything else, but don't forget their food needs care too. If you don't use a whole tin at once, transfer what's left to a covered container that you don't use for any other purpose. Dried food can be left out if your pet doesn't eat it all at once, but any kind of moist food, home-cooked or tinned, will soon attract insects if it's left standing in a warm kitchen. You have to be even more careful if you leave pet food outdoors, where it's an ideal spot for flies to lay their eggs.

Food poisoning from fruit and veg, though rare, is increasing as out-of-season produce is flown in from farther away. Just occasionally it can pass on parasites: worms and other little organisms that live in your body and can make you run down or ill. Healthy though salads are, they really have to be well washed – unlike cooked vegetables, they won't go through any cleansing heat treatment.

In fact, it's a good idea to wash produce even if you're going to cook it, since heat doesn't kill all germs. This also gives you a chance to pick out any insects, grit or anything else that might be hiding in the leaves. Fruit and vegetables may have been sprayed with yet more pesticide after harvesting, then waxed. Scrub fruit and veg in warm soapy water, or the special washes available in health food shops, using a stiff brush kept for this purpose only. Make certain you've got all the wax off, if there's any, then rinse everything well. It's advisable to peel root vegetables, though this isn't the complete answer since some of the pesticide residues may have permeated all the way through. Most of the vitamins are just beneath the skin, too. The best answer really is to buy organic root vegetables that have been raised in clean soil without the use of chemicals. Even these need at least a rinse, to remove any grime they've picked up since they left the farm.

Some keen cooks went off the idea of making preserves after hearing about some fatal cases of botulism in the States. In fact, those were caused by home canning, something that is rarely prac-tised here. The danger there is in not being able to heat the food, in its can, enough to kill off the deadly clostridium botulinum. Home-made jams and chutneys are boiled before being put in jars – so as long as the jars and their lids are clean, there's rarely any problem.

IMPORTANT POINTS

- Wash your hands before you cook, after touching raw meat or seafood, and before you eat.
- Don't let any other food touch a knife, or chopping board, or container you've used for raw meat.
- Wash or peel all fresh produce.

Thawing times
The Food Safety Advisory Centre recommends the following times for safe thawing.
1.5kg = 3.3lb, 2.5cm = 1 inch, 3kg = 6.6lb, 450g = 1lb

	In a fridge	In a cool room	In a microwave
Poultry			
Whole birds	5-8 hrs per 450g, minimum 24 hrs	2.5-3.5 hrs per 450g, minimum 9hrs	9-12 mins per 450g
Poultry portions	6-8 hrs	Not recommended	6-10 mins per piece
Other meat			
Joints over 1.5kg	6-7 hrs per 450g	2-3 hrs per 450g	9-12 mins per 450g
Joints under 1.5kg	3-4 hrs per 450g	1-2 hrs per 450g	9-12 mins per 450g
Steak or chops 2.5cm thick	5-6 hrs	2-4 hrs	6-10 mins per piece
Fish			
Whole fish or thick portions	4-5 hrs per 450g	1-2 hrs per 450g	5 mins per 450g
Thin flat fish or fillets	3-4 hrs per 450g or cook from frozen	1-2 hrs per 450g or cook from frozen	5 mins per 450g or cook from frozen
Vegetables	Cook from frozen		
Prepared meals	Follow manufacturer's instructions		

EQUIPMENT

An array of gleaming copper saucepans looks good on the kitchen wall, but you'd be wise to leave them there as decorations, unless they're lined with stainless steel. Some of the metal from saucepans and frying pans can leach into the food you're cooking, and copper can actually cause sickness and diarrhoea. Aluminium, which most cheap saucepans are made of, has been linked with Alzheimer's Disease. It's not a definitely proven cause, but people who have died with Alzheimer's have been found to have aluminium in their brains.

Why not reduce the risks by replacing your copper and aluminium saucepans with stainless steel? You don't have to lose the excellent heat-conducting qualities that make copper and aluminium so convenient to cook with. Sandwich-based saucepans are fine: a layer of aluminium or copper placed between two layers of steel will distribute heat evenly. This way the sandwiched metal doesn't come in contact with the food. If you love your aluminium pots too much to bin them, just don't cook anything acidic in them, like tomatoes or fruit.

Many serious cooks swear by cast-iron pots, which cook very slowly and evenly. Some of the iron can leach into your food, but that shouldn't be a problem unless you have a rare medical condition like haemochromatosis, in which iron accumulates dangerously in your body. For women it could even be a bonus, topping up iron stores that are so often unhealthily low. A more everyday hazard with cast iron is that it weighs a ton, so be prepared for this before you take a laden pan off the stove and put your back out.

Glassware and enamel (which is made from glass) are safe choices for saucepans, since glass does not react with food in any way. Even if you use metal saucepans for other foods, anything acidic like fruit should be cooked in an enamel or glassware saucepan, to avoid the risk of metal poisoning. You have to take a little extra care to avoid chipping enamel saucepans or dishes, since they are more fragile than metal. Once they're chipped it's best not to use them, since germs can hide in the chipped part. You wouldn't put hot glassware pans into cold water, but beware of even putting

Never store food in a metal saucepan

them down on a cold draining board, since they have been known to shatter there too. Never store food in a metal saucepan, but transfer it as soon as it's cooked into a container made of china, enamel or heatproof glass.

Nonstick surfaces used to have a safety question mark over them, since they could flake off into food. Modern nonsticks shouldn't do this, though any flakes that do slip into your food are said to pass through the body undigested. It's still a good idea to use wooden or special nonstick utensils with these pans to avoid damaging them, since one scrape can destroy their nonstick qualities. Also, never heat a nonstick pan when it's empty since you risk releasing toxic fumes. It's easy to do by accident, especially when you're cooking with electricity, and it can damage any kind of cookware.

The pressure cooker is an old standby that now has a bad image. Many a cook in the 1940s and '50s cowered behind the door while the pressure cooker made menacing noises and, occasionally, exploded. No one who had cleaned the remains of dinner off the walls, floor and ceiling could ever feel quite safe with one of those monsters again. Luckily, modern pressure cookers are a lot safer than their early counterparts. They still have all the advantages of pressure cooking – it's fast, uses just a little water and preserves vitamins as well as flavour. But with newer safety valves, explosions are almost unheard of.

Slow cookers are a boon to people who are out all day and need a meal ready when they come home. Just throw in the ingredients and let them stew at a leisurely pace while you're at work. It's the best way to tenderise cheap cuts of meat, too. But do make sure that it does reach the seventy degrees C that's needed to kill off any bacteria in the meat. If you're not sure about what temperature it reaches, take a few minutes before you go out to boil up the meat first. As long as it goes straight in the slow cooker and doesn't have time to cool, it should then be fine.

Microwave ovens offer a simple answer when you're in a hurry. They cook food at top speed without sacrificing vitamins or other nutrients. But some scientists believe microwaves could give out harmful radiation. No one is yet sure whether this is harmful, or how much microwave radiation is safe, and from what distance. Sounds silly? People laughed when scientists first warned about radiation from mobile phones, but these have now been linked with brain tumours. For this reason it's probably a good idea not to stand within a couple of feet of a microwave when it's in use. This may one day prove to be an unnecessary precaution. But it's a simple one, so there's no harm in following it. If your microwave is old or secondhand, check

> *If your microwave is old or secondhand, check that the door still closes perfectly and the seal is intact*

that the door still closes perfectly and the seal is intact. Your local council's Public Health Department may also be able to tell you whether your model is still considered safe.

You also have to take care you're using the microwave correctly. Most forms of cooking give you a bit of leeway in learning how to use them best. Remember the old maxim 'When all else fails, read the instructions'? With microwaves you really do need to read the instructions before all else fails. It's pretty obvious when a frying pan catches fire, but you can use a microwave wrongly for a long time without discovering it. Defrosting for example: instructions vary according to the model, but if you don't follow them exactly you could be part-cooking the food before it's defrosted, with obvious food-poisoning risks. Always leave food to stand for the length of time specified, since it will be continuing to cook. Then cut it open for a visual check that it's well done.

Don't use any materials in it that aren't microwave safe. You can buy special containers, thermometers and even cling film that won't harm the microwave or your food. A microwave will give out noisy sparks if you put metal in it, but china with a metallic glaze or pattern could damage the oven without your noticing.

Though good-quality cookware is more expensive, it's an investment worth making. For a start, you shouldn't have to keep replacing it. It should keep its shape instead of buckling, and that's a positive safety point, since many kitchen burns are caused by saucepans tipping over. It will also cook more evenly, helping to ensure food isn't left with dangerous half-cooked spots. Look for firmly attached handles to avoid accidents: riveted ones should be strongest.

Good-quality knives are vital too, and not even expensive. As everyone discovers when they finally dump their cheap, easily blunted knives, cooking becomes magically easier. You're more likely to take the trouble to cook fresh vegetables when chopping them is no longer such a chore. It's also safer: a blunt knife blade is actually more like to cut you than a sharp one, since you can't control it and the blade slips more readily than it slices.

There's no need to spend a fortune on top-quality kitchenware, though. If you buy one well-made saucepan at a time, you may find you don't need all the options of a full set. On a tight budget, you can get away with just one good all-purpose chopping knife and another for the meat.

IMPORTANT POINTS

- Follow microwave instructions to the letter.
- Don't leave food in metal saucepans after it's been cooked.
- If you use a slow cooker, check that it reaches a high enough temperature to make meat safe.

COOKING

When it comes to cooking, it's bad news for those who like their steak rare. To avoid the risk of food poisoning caused by a number of different bacteria, meat should always be cooked through. This means checking that it's well done in the middle, and that the juices are running clear. If the meat is still slightly red, it needs more cooking. And unless you're eating certified organic meat, cut off the fat. That's not just for your heart and your figure, but because it's more likely to contain chemical residues. Also, instead of traditional stuffed poultry, cook the stuffing separately and serve it beside the bird. Packed inside, it can stop the meat cooking through, and bacteria from the raw meat may survive in the stuffing.

If you cook a lot of meat, it may be worth investing in a meat thermometer, to make sure it is seventy to seventy-seven degrees C at the centre. This is especially useful with microwave ovens, which may not cook food all the way through – you can buy special microwave thermometers with no metal parts. When you use the microwave, you should heat food for at least two minutes and cut it open to check that the inside is piping hot and visibly cooked.

> *It may be worth investing in a meat thermometer*

Remember that these days British eggs have to be well done too – irritating if you like them soft-boiled with soldiers. Cooks should watch out too for recipes like meringues, mousses, zabaglione and some kinds of ice-cream. Shop-bought versions should be safer, since they're likely to contain pasteurised eggs, but check the labels to make sure. Organic eggs are produced in healthier conditions, so are less likely to carry disease, but even they can't be guaranteed safe. Some experts advise everyone to cut out anything, shop-bought or home-made, that contains uncooked or lightly cooked egg. Even if you're willing to take the chance, anyone who needs to err on the side of caution (the very old or young, pregnant women and anyone unwell) should avoid even the commercial varieties of their favourite treats unless they've checked the only eggs contained in the ingredients are pasteurised.

You can test eggs for freshness by putting them into a bowl of water: if they stand on end, they're stale, and if they float you should dispose of them very carefully. Don't break the shell or you may be hit by that horrific rotten-egg smell. When you break a fresh egg, the yolk is rounded rather than flat on top. Though freshness is no indicator that an egg isn't infected, the older it is the more time bacteria have had to multiply to dangerous levels.

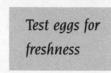

Test eggs for freshness

All cooks taste the food as they go along – that's why recipes say 'adjust the seasoning'. You'd need to have cooked the same dish an awful lot of times before you stop needing to check the taste. But do use a clean teaspoon each time, rather than dipping the same one back in.

When you're using any kind of frozen food from a packet, say frozen peas, always measure out the quantity you need into a cup and put the packet straight back into the freezer. This avoids partially defrosting the food in the packet every time you empty it into a steaming saucepan and gives you a chance to check through the food for quality. This practice once saved me from cooking a frozen slug.

IMPORTANT POINTS

- Make sure food (especially meat) is well cooked throughout.
- Serve it up as soon as possible. Most problems stem from reheating things or keeping them warm – so eat hot food hot and cold food cold.

AROUND THE KITCHEN

Dish washers are handy if you don't like washing up, but they're not essential for food hygiene. A good scrub in hot soapy water is enough. Everything should be rinsed, too, to get rid of any chemical residues from the detergent. A second sink, maybe half sized, or an extra washing up bowl lets you rinse them without wasting hot running water.

Even though some things don't look as if they need a proper wash, say if you've just had a glass of water or drained vegetables through a colander, those should be washed up properly too. Cutlery washed in cold water is a well known culprit for passing hepatitis among budget travellers eating in little cafés in remote parts of the world. Other germs spread that way too, such as those which cause colds and sore throats. No need to dry up though: the air is at least as clean as any tea towel.

Work surfaces need to be wiped and cleaned as you go along, using cloths rinsed in hot soapy water. When you've finished the washing up, wring out your kitchen cloths in the hot water and hang them to dry. If you leave cloths or sponges damp they get slimy and smelly, so wring them as dry as possible after each use. And remember not to pass germs around. This is an often overlooked area of food safety: you could easily transfer bacteria on to a clean surface by wiping it with a cloth that's touched, say, the meat chopping board.

When you've finished cooking, wipe the cooker and work surfaces with kitchen cleaner. Keep walls and work surfaces free from cracks, so germs have nowhere to hide, and throw away any deeply scored chopping boards or chipped crockery. (If you can't bear to part with favourite pieces of china, you can always keep it for decoration only – old mugs make pretty, informal flower vases.) The waste bin should have a well-fitting lid, kept tightly shut, and be emptied before it starts to overflow. Anything that gets spilt should be mopped up quickly, since it attracts insects. Even spills in the fridge are a breeding ground for bacteria.

Most important of all, wash your hands – when you come in from outside, after going to the loo, after handling raw meat, after blowing your nose, after touching the rubbish bin or stroking a pet, and always before you start cooking or eating. You can pick up germs from anything you touch. Luckily, soap and warm water will send practically all of them safely down

Having a cold is a very good excuse for getting someone else to do the cooking

the drain. Keep a separate hand towel so you never wipe your fingers on the tea towel, and wash both of them frequently.

If you've cut your finger, keep a waterproof plaster on while you're handling food. And needless to say, don't sneeze anywhere near uncovered food – you could spread food poisoning bacteria as well as the cold virus. In fact, having a cold is a very good excuse for getting someone else to do the cooking. After all, they wouldn't want to take the risk, would they?

Despite all the dangers of the outside world, most accidents happen in the home, and of these most take place in the kitchen. So always be aware of kitchen safety, especially with children around. Electric leads are a hazard trailing across any floor, but more so in a kitchen where you're likely to be carrying hot food or boiling water when you trip over them. Place saucepans on the stove where the handles won't either stick out or be heated by another ring. Work surfaces and floors should be easy to clean, so dirt doesn't have a chance to build up.

A cooker standing on its own is dangerous, since you have nowhere to put pans when you take them off the heat. You'll be constantly reaching across open space, at risk of slopping food on to the floor, where it'll become a slippery hazard, or on to passing children or animals. The safest and most convenient layout has the cooker, sink and fridge in an L-shape along two walls, or all in a row, with a continuous work surface between them. This allows the least possible risk of dropping or spilling things as you move from one to another.

IMPORTANT POINTS

- If you store food correctly (and for as short a time as possible), cook it thoroughly and eat it as soon as it's ready, you should avoid most risks.
- Don't forget to change towels regularly, and wash and dry kitchen cloths too.
- Take extra care with food safety if you're cooking for someone in one of the vulnerable categories: old, very young, pregnant or unwell.

WATER

Tap water may be healthier than you think. On average less than one per cent contains bacteria, and most experts believe it's safe to drink straight from the tap. (That's the cold tap, of course: don't drink water that's been kept warm in a tank.) Still, a kitchen filter reduces your risk of drinking unwanted metals and chemical residues that run off farmers' fields into the water supply. Look for a filter that removes pesticides, chlorine, lead and copper. Best results come from expensive filtration systems that have to be plumbed into your sink, but even a cheap jug model should improve the taste of water and filter out limescale along with some chemicals. The safest buy is one that will fit in the fridge, since bacteria quickly start to breed in water that's left standing around in a warm room. Be careful to replace the water every day and change the filter as often as instructed. If you keep using the filter after it stops working, bacteria will multiply in it and you'll end up worse off than drinking straight from the tap.

> *Tap water may be healthier than you think*

What if the water company announces it's found something nasty like Cryptosporidium in the supply, and warns customers to boil their drinking water? Keeping water to a rolling boil for one minute is the best way of killing this parasite. The well-boiled water can be stored in the fridge in screw-top bottles that have been carefully washed and rinsed, also with boiled water. When there's a water scare on, don't forget to boil the water for ice cubes as well as for washing fruit and veg.

Lead leached from pipes can be a problem, especially in Scotland, where both lead pipes and soft water are common-place. If you live in an old house with lead pipes in a soft-water area, to flush out any lead run the tap fast for thirty seconds in the morning and again when you've been out all day. How can you find out? Soft water is the sort that's easy to lather and hard to rinse off: when you wash your hair in soft water a small blob of shampoo creates a huge froth-hat, but you have to rinse several times before your hair squeaks. Soft water, rather than hard water, is more likely to pick up a tinge of lead from the pipes. As for the pipes, your local council should be able to tell you the material from which they are made.

Bottled waters aren't necessarily healthier, though: some have been found to contain more bacteria than you'd ever get from the tap. The law controls only the amount of bacteria they're allowed to contain when they're bottled – they may then sit around unrefrigerated for eighteen months before they're sold, with bacteria multiplying inside. Sparkling water is safer than still, since the carbon dioxide that adds the fizz stops bacteria growing so fast.

Labels can be misleading, too. 'Mineral water' has to come from a specific mineral source. It doesn't have to contain any specific quantity of minerals, and rarely includes enough to be worth using as a mineral supplement. It is only allowed to be filtered (and carbonated, if it's sold as 'sparkling'). But 'table water' or 'spring water' can come from anywhere, including straight from the tap – and they frequently do. They have to meet the same standards as tap water, and may be filtered and treated to kill bacteria. If you're going to drink tap water, you might as well get it fresh from your own tap for a fraction of the price. In pubs, ask for a brand-name bottled water: it's less likely to be out of the tap. And if you're trying to cut down on salt in your diet, because of high blood pressure for example, check the labels since some mineral waters are high in sodium.

It's only worth buying drinks that claim to be 'spring water with a hint of fruit' if you really like the taste. Look closely at the label and you're likely to find a string of ingredients, including sweeteners, making these basically soft drinks. Nothing wrong with that, as long as you know you're buying a soft drink – it's just not an especially healthy option.

IMPORTANT POINTS

- Change filters as often as the instructions say.
- Let the cold tap run for thirty seconds before you first use the water, if you have lead pipes.
- Except when something's gone wrong with your mains water supply, only buy bottled water if you prefer the taste.
- Don't drink bottled water that's passed its best-before date. It could contain high levels of bacteria.
- If you're on a low salt diet and drink mineral water, look for brands containing less than 20mg sodium per litre.

CHAPTER FOUR

Eating away from home

BARBECUES

Eating out of doors brings hazards of its own, and not just because of the flies that home in from miles around. Eating burnt or charred meat has been linked with an increased risk of cancer. More immediately, food-poisoning bacteria have a field day at outdoor meals.

Cooked food and salads sit around in the hot sun. The chicken gets burnt outside while the inside stays half-done. Without a water supply at hand it's inconvenient to keep washing utensils and hands, and sauces and mayonnaise warm up nicely (for the bacteria, that is). And to cap it all the dog seizes every chance to sniff around the sausages when your back is turned.

One ally at a barbecue is the marinade: the vinegar has a slight antibacterial effect as well as improving taste and texture, so make plenty in advance to steep the meat in. Making a bit of space on each side of the barbie before you start helps to keep the raw meat separate from the cooked food. If you get into the habit of

> *One ally at a barbecue is the marinade*

using, say, blue utensils for raw food and red ones for anything that's been cooked, it's easier to keep the two sets safely apart. And there's no harm in cheating a bit, by half-cooking the meat indoors and bringing it straight out to finish off on the barbie, as long as it doesn't hang around between the two stages. Before you serve each piece of meat, cut it open to check it's done all the way through – especially the chicken.

Salads work best if you keep them in the fridge, bringing out one smaller bowlful at a time. Fill a fresh bowl each time rather than topping up the one that's been standing out in the sun. You don't need dozens of salad bowls; just enlist someone to wash the bowls up between refills. This way the salad is colder and crisper, as well as safer. Mayonnaise and sauces, too, should be brought out in small quantities, so they don't have a chance to stand around long.

Food shouldn't stand around uncovered, but how do you cover objects like salad bowls and jugs? The Victorians had the answer: they crocheted delicate cotton covers, with beads to hold down the edges. These days, you can find similar things on craft stalls and in gift catalogues to keep wasps out of the fruit salad and flies off the meat.

Incidentally, if you're putting out bowls of carrot and celery sticks to use as dips, cut them too short for people to dip in twice. It's the same with drinking from a bottle and putting it back in the fridge, or taking a spoonful from a dish and dipping it in again – your saliva has now been mixed with the contents. Even if no one else is going to share that food or drink, you've introduced bacteria that could multiply before you finish it.

PICNICS

Part of the fun of a day in the country is finding your own food. Books such as Richard Mabey's Food for Free (see Resources, page 137) introduce a wealth of treats to pick for yourself. Needless to say, if you're not sure what something is, don't put it in your mouth. Some of the juiciest-looking berries could give you a bad stomach ache or worse. Blackberries are one thing even the least countrywise townie can recognise. Eat and enjoy them, as long as they're not beside a main road, or looking sick and shrivelled, as if they've been sprayed with weed-killer (not everyone appreciates them).

Mushrooms are a delicious gift from the countryside, but you really do need a specialist book to identify the good ones: every year a few people poison themselves with the wrong kind of mushroom. If gathering fresh shellfish is part of a day out on the beach for you, make sure the water isn't polluted. Remote beaches tend to be the safest spots, but estuaries are risky.

Wrapped ice-creams are safer than soft-whip cones from machines, which can easily breed bacteria.

When you're taking a packed meal with you, carry food in insulated containers. If you're going to be out for long before eating, you may want to forgo the cold chicken and paté in favour of fresh crusty bread, hard cheeses, olives, cherry tomatoes and other treats that are more tolerant of warm weather. Then you can spend the money you saved on some favourite drinks – after all, no one has ever been poisoned by a bottle of champagne.

> *Carry food in insulated containers*

RESTAURANTS, CAFÉS AND TAKEAWAYS

When you're away from home you have less control over the way your food is handled, so look out for clean premises. You may not be able to see the kitchen, but if any part of the place looks dirty or run down you can make a reasonable guess that the parts you can't see are no better. In restaurants, the loos give a fair indication of hygiene standards. Is there toilet paper, soap, a clean towel or hand dryer? Are the wash basins clean? If the customer loos aren't well kept, facilities for the staff are likely to be even worse – and if they don't have soap and clean towels, their hands will be depositing germs on to your food. In sandwich shops, check how the staff handle food. If they pick it up with their fingers, go somewhere else. The same if they or the counter look grubby or untidy.

If you're tempted by a supermarket salad bar, remember that food may have been sitting out under the shop lights for hours. Despite the air-conditioning, it is a lot warmer in a shop than in a fridge. Even though separate servers are provided, people tend to dip the same one in several tubs, giving any bugs plenty of chance to get around. Coleslaw and other salads have been known to carry listeria when the ingredients weren't properly washed and the salad had stood around for a while. Mayonnaise is as good a growth culture for bacteria as you could find in a laboratory, so choose salads in vinaigrette-type dressings instead. Avoid those containing meat or fish – buy a packet of ham to go with them instead. If you buy salad later than lunch time, remember that it could have been sitting under the shop's warm lights all day.

In pubs, thinking of your figure is just one good reason to leave any open bowls of nuts or crisps alone. One study found traces of twelve different people's urine on the peanuts sitting on a pub bar: people had gone to the loo, not washed their hands, picked up a few peanuts on the way back to their table … but, of course, they're only put there to make you thirsty so you buy more drinks.

Takeaways are blamed for a lot of food-poisoning cases. But the true culprit is often the least obvious suspect – not the curried prawns or the sweet-and-sour pork but the innocent-looking rice. Rice that's been reheated or kept warm is the perfect breeding ground for bacillus cereus, a powerful food-poisoning bug that multiplies at extraordinary speed. Even freshly fried rice isn't safe if it was kept for long after the original boiling. So make sure yours is hot and looks fresh and moist, without any slight crust or overcooked grains.

CHAPTER FIVE

Safe for your family

I t can be unnerving trying to feed a family when every day seems to bring another health risk. Not that they're all new – we're just finding out more about them. Pregnant women have been warned to avoid certain foods for fear of miscarriage or birth defects. Babies and children are more vulnerable than adults since they're still growing, and their small bodies have less well-developed defences. Luckily it's the same story as with food poisoning: a few simple precautions cut out most of the danger.

PREGNANCY

This is a time when good-quality food counts more than ever, helping the baby to develop as well as nourishing you. You should actually start taking folic acid supplements before you conceive: it helps prevent birth defects such as spina bifida, but starting when you know you're pregnant may be too late. Since not many of us know when we're going to conceive in three months' time, it's worth taking folic acid if there's any chance you might get pregnant. A 400mcg daily supplement is safe for women to take long term, even if they're not planning a pregnancy.

Most women know not to eat soft, mould-ripened cheese when they're pregnant: listeria has caused too many miscarriages and stillbirths to be worth risking. (See 'Who is most at risk', page 112, for more details.) Cook-chilled meals and chicken that's sold ready to eat are supposed to be safe if you heat them till they're piping hot. But you may prefer to give these a miss till after the baby's born. You also need to be more careful than most people with raw egg. Mayonnaise and meringues may be worth the risk at other times, but not when you're pregnant.

Peanuts are also best avoided while you're pregnant or breastfeeding. It is now known that children can be born allergic to substances their mothers used a lot during the pregnancy. Peanuts seem to be a common culprit, perhaps because peanut oil is also found in bottle-milk and nipple creams. They cause a particularly dangerous allergy, so they're worth avoiding – remembering that peanut oil is also contained in many processed foods. For the same reason, try not to binge too much on one food while you're pregnant.

> *Peanuts are also best avoided while you're pregnant or breastfeeding*

Liver is so packed with vitamin A that it can actually be dangerous when you're pregnant, since an overdose of vitamin A can cause birth defects. True, the only known cases have involved women either eating huge amounts of liver every day or taking vitamin A supplements, but to be on the safe side it's best not to eat a lot of liver (or liver products such as paté) if you're pregnant, and definitely not to take vitamin A supplements. A daily multivitamin should be all right, since it shouldn't exceed recommended doses: just check on the label to make sure.

It's a pity really, since liver is also full of the extra iron you need when you're carrying. Doctors used to dose pregnant women with iron supplements routinely, but the latest thinking is that you probably don't need them unless you're obviously short of iron. You can keep your levels topped up naturally by eating plenty of meat, fish, wholemeal bread, margarine, dried fruit and fortified breakfast cereals. Vegetables are good sources of iron too, especially watercress, broccoli, green peppers, kidney beans, tomatoes, salad leaves and other greens, sunflower seeds and sesame seeds. If you do have to take an iron supplement, those in liquid form are less likely to cause constipation.

Needless to say, it's not a good idea to drink alcohol or take any other drugs when you're pregnant, since these can harm the baby. Heavy drinking early in pregnancy can cause very serious birth defects, but unfortunately this can happen before you know you're pregnant. Still, it makes sense to stop drinking as soon as you miss a period. Some women don't have any choice: the very smell of alcohol or even coffee when they're pregnant makes them feel sick. Some experts say the odd glass of wine later in pregnancy won't do any harm. Others disagree, on the grounds that anything you eat or drink goes into the baby's bloodstream too – and you wouldn't put alcohol in a baby's bottle. If you've miscarried, or had a difficult pregnancy in the past, it's worth being extra cautious.

Even medicines can be harmful, so check with your doctor before taking any. If you have to take regular medication, let your GP or specialist know when you start planning a pregnancy so you can discuss any changes you may need to make.

Toxoplasmosis, spread by cats, is another risk pregnant women need to avoid. It's not very common, so it certainly doesn't mean you should say goodbye to your cat. The measures you take to avoid toxoplasmosis are part of normal kitchen hygiene anyway – just be especially careful to observe them if you're pregnant, or cooking for someone who is. It's also carried on unwashed fruit and vegetables or undercooked meat, so make sure the produce is washed and the meat well done. Wash your hands after stroking the cat and before you eat or prepare food. One extra thing pregnant women should do, though, is to get someone else to take out the cat litter and clean up any mess the cat makes. That's a risk you shouldn't take.

FEEDING A BABY

Scares about contaminated infant formula have shaken women's faith in bottle feeding. First we read in a government report in May 1996 that phthalates, the 'gender-bending' chemicals that are known to reduce fertility in animals, had been discovered in fifteen brands of formula. Then one brand was found to contain salmonella.

Bottle feeding is a major killer of Third World babies, increasing their risk of death twenty-five fold according to UNICEF, the United Nations children's organisation. Of course, the water supply over here is a lot safer, but bottle feeding is still the main cause of gastroenteritis among babies. That's not just because it is tempting to skimp on the fiddly routine of sterilising equipment and preparing feeds. Bottle-fed babies have less resistance to disease than those who are breastfed. They get five to ten times more stomach upsets, twice as many chest infections, many more painful urinary tract infections and are still suffering more allergies and wheeziness even when they reach school.

Breast milk contains the antibodies the mother produces to protect herself from infection and even includes a kind of natural antibiotic. The content and consistency of breast milk varies naturally to meet the baby's changing needs. Unlike cow's milk, it is made for human babies. Even if any pollutants (or infections) have entered the mother's milk, its other benefits still make it a healthier feed than formula milk.

The only time breast milk can harm a child is if the mother is passing on something like AIDS, herpes or hepatitis. Just ask your health visitor if you're worried about any other ailment. If you have to take any medicines, check with your doctor that it's still all right to breastfeed – there are a few, including some migraine drugs, that might cause problems. The baby can cope if you have an occasional alcoholic drink or coffee, but in general don't take in anything you don't want to share with the baby.

> *If you have to take any medicines, check with your doctor that it's still all right to breastfeed*

Many new mothers want to breastfeed, since it's cheap, convenient and far better for the baby. Sometimes breast-feeding is difficult, but much of the problem is caused by holding the baby in the wrong position. Amazingly, even many nurses on maternity wards do not know how to hold a baby properly to feed, and the Consumers' Association found that the diagrams given to doctors, midwives and new mothers showing how to breastfeed were almost all inaccurate. That means most new mothers have been taught the wrong way, which is why they eventually give up.

It's worth persevering even if you think you're not producing enough milk, since the more the baby feeds the more milk you will automatically make – even if there is a bit of a timelag at first. Breastfed babies do tend to drink more because it's so easily digested. Some women even express milk to feed their babies when they go back to work.

> *Breastfed babies do tend to drink more*

The baby-milk companies who sponsor so much official litera-
ture about breastfeeding make it all sound terribly hard work, but
they would, wouldn't they? It takes courage to stick with it when
people around you suggest giving up. So contact the Association
of Breastfeeding Mothers, the La Leche League or the National
Childbirth Trust for some valuable help and advice (see Resources,
page 138). They'll put you in touch with an experienced counsel-
lor who has been through it all herself, and they can even provide
practical support such as the hire of breast pumps.

The odd bottle-feed can be useful, but be careful how often
you do it – the less often you breastfeed the less milk you will
produce. If you're planning to use a bottle sometimes (or a
dummy), wait a few weeks till breastfeeding is well established.
They're a different shape from your nipple and require a
different sucking action, so they may stop your baby learning
how to suck properly at the breast.

TIPS FOR SUCCESSFUL
BREASTFEEDING

Start as soon as possible, preferably with an hour of the birth.
Even before the milk comes in you'll produce a watery fluid
called colostrum that is good for the baby. And this helps you to
establish a good supply from the beginning.

Sit in a comfortable chair, with a footstool if you prefer, and
hold the baby facing you, rather than lying sideways on as for
bottle feeding. You may find it more comfortable with a pillow
on your lap to support the baby so that your arms don't get
tired. Lift the baby to your nipple rather than leaning down, and
if the baby isn't showing an interest, gently stroke her lower lip
with your nipple. When she opens her mouth, let her take as big
a mouthful of your nipple as she can.

The nipple really needs to go about an inch in, with baby's
mouth wide open. People used to worry that babies could suffo-

cate while feeding, so women were advised to hold the breast back with their fingers – a recipe for failure and sore nipples into the bargain. Some babies feed better in the 'football hold': still holding the baby facing you, support the back of her neck with your hand and slip her legs under your arm beside the breast you're offering her, with her feet towards your back. This is a good position for babies who don't readily latch on to the breast.

If your nipples get sore, it's usually because they're not going far enough into the baby's mouth, so encourage her to take a good mouthful. Other ways to avoid sore nipples include letting them dry uncovered after feeding, and rubbing them with a little breast milk or nipple cream if they feel too dry. When you want to change breasts, don't pull the baby away (ouch), break the suction by slipping a finger between her gums.

To prevent engorgement – your breasts becoming painfully swollen with milk – let the baby feed frequently and on demand until your supply adjusts naturally to her needs. If they do become swollen, take over-the-counter painkillers and apply warm, wet compresses till they've eased.

Don't give supplementary feeds, since your own supply should catch up with the baby's needs within a couple of days. Some women drink a glass of carrot juice every day

Drink a glass of carrot juice every day

to increase their milk yield: not a conventional method, but it won't do the baby any harm and it'll certainly be good for you.

IMPORTANT POINTS

- A woman who breastfeeds gets her figure back faster, while reducing her own risk of breast cancer and possibly ovarian cancer too.
- You'll need about 500 extra calories a day and lots of water to drink, to replenish your own reserves.

BOTTLE SAFETY

Bottle feeding needs a lot of organising to keep everything clean and safe. Since a bottle-fed baby doesn't have any natural immunity to disease, you have to be prepared to deal with more bouts of sniffles and tummy bugs than if you're breastfeeding. But doing everything by the book cuts down the risk of stomach upsets at least.

IMPORTANT POINTS

- You'll need at least six bottles and teats, plus sterilising equipment, a bottle brush and mixing jug. None of these should be used for anything else. A bottle warmer is useful but not vital.
- Sterilise the equipment between uses, following the instructions.
- When you're preparing a feed, let the tap run for at least two minutes before using the water, then bring the water to the boil and let it cool before mixing the formula. Don't reboil water, since some of it evaporates and leaves higher concentrations of minerals in what's left.
- If you have a water softener, don't use water from this for the baby since it may contain too much of the mineral sodium. Non-fizzy bottled water should be safe as long as it contains less than 20mg sodium per litre (the label should say), but you still need to boil it and let it cool.
- Measure out the formula exactly: too much can make the baby dehydrated, but too little won't give enough nourishment. Don't add sugar or anything else, just formula and water.
- If you need to heat the bottle, stand it in a saucepan of hot water. Don't put it in the microwave, as hot spots can burn the baby's mouth.
- When you go out, take made-up bottles in an insulated bag with packs of ice.

- Throw away any leftover made-up milk because bacteria breed in it very quickly.
- Hold the bottle so that the teat is full of milk and the baby isn't gulping air.
- Never leave a baby alone with a bottle, even for a couple of minutes, since they can choke very easily.
- Never feed a baby on anything other than breast milk or infant formula – the baby's system isn't mature enough to digest anything else.
- Soya milk isn't recommended for babies because it contains phytoestrogens, which are suspected of being able to damage a baby's reproductive system.

BABY FOODS

In the past, toddlers would be weaned on the same plain meat-and-veg foods their parents ate, just mashed up. Now we buy them special foods in tins and jars. Some of these ranges, like Baby Organix or HiPP, really are wholesome food. But many are full of cheap fillers like maltodextrin, plus too much sugar and salt.

Organic baby foods – free from chemicals, drugs, irradiation and genetically modified organisms – are available in most branches of Waitrose, Safeway and Sainsbury's, and in some Co-ops and Tescos. Many smaller shops and supermarkets also stock organic baby foods, and may be more responsive to requests from customers who would like to buy them.

More children seem to develop food allergies now than ever before. We can only guess at the reasons, but one theory is that children are being introduced to substances like wheat and peanut oil earlier than in the past, since these are present in baby foods. Why not just share some of your own food with the baby, when he's old enough? Apart from costing a fraction of what you'd spend on baby foods, this ensures he's getting wholesome food without lots of additives (as long as you are).

The safest action is to breastfeed as long as possible. Up till the age of four months, a baby shouldn't be given anything other than breast or formula milk: even ordinary cow's milk is too hard for a baby to digest and doesn't contain enough nutrients.

From four to six months old you can start trying some new foods, whizzed in the liquidiser or pushed through a strainer. Milk will still be the baby's main food, but he'll start getting used to the idea of other tastes. From the age of six months you can start offering more solid foods, especially meat and iron-rich vegetables, before the baby's milk feed. You'll still need to mash them up, but less finely than before, and you can start adding finger foods like bread. From the age of nine months, baby can share family meals and snacks, still topping up with breast or formula milk. After a year, he can have his first taste of cow's milk and switch from feeders to ordinary cups. But don't worry if things seem to be taking longer. Babies don't run to anyone else's timetable. You can discuss any concerns with your health visitor or ring the National Childbirth Trust (see Resources, page 138) for advice.

> *Share some of your own food with the baby, when he's old enough*

IMPORTANT POINTS

- Babies under four months old should only be given breast or formula milk – no cow's milk and no solids.
- When weaning, don't give them salt, sugar or fatty meats. Try to avoid processed foods.
- After six months old, a baby can drink water or diluted fruit juice. Avoid soft drinks (they rot children's teeth), tea or coffee.
- Stay close to babies and small children when they're eating, in case they start choking.
- Don't give cow's milk to a baby under a year old.

What can a baby eat?

The Department of Health recommends trying these and other similar foods, to find out what your baby likes.

Birth to four months	
Breast or formula milk only	
Four months	**Six months**
Everything is pureed or liquidised	Grated hard cheese
Potato, yam and other root vegetables	Wholemeal bread
Rice	Unsweetened breakfast cereals
Lean meat	Tinned pineapple
Beans or peas	Fish or fish fingers (check very carefully for bones)
Cabbage, sprouts, cauliflower	Eggs: well-cooked, scrambled, or hard-boiled and mashed
Banana	Vegetables as before, now roughly mashed
Apple	
Pear	
Plum	
Melon	

SAFE FOOD FOR CHILDREN

Even the most wholesome food may be unsuitable for a baby or a small child, because their digestion can't yet cope with it. Acid fruits like strawberries, for example, are too harsh for under-twos. And fruits of all kind, vital though they are, have to be prepared carefully for small children to avoid pips and cores.

Fatty meats like pork, too, are hard for a child to digest. Fish is a healthy food for a growing child, but you have to watch out for those fine bones. Even adults can choke on these, so stick with fillets unless you have the patience to go through carefully removing every little bone. With small children, you should even check fillets to make sure. Don't give them smoked fish: it contains preservatives called nitrates and nitrites, which have been banned from baby and toddler foods. Smoked or cured meats (like ham and bacon) are off the menu for the same reason. They're also too salty for a child.

In fact, it's best not to add salt to a child's food. They don't need any, though unfortunately it's already added to most processed food. Salt can overload a small child's kidneys, with harmful results. For the same reason they shouldn't drink mineral water, since their kidneys haven't yet developed enough to deal with the minerals it contains. Other bottled water should be safe – though it should still be boiled for children under eight months.

Whole or chopped nuts and seeds are easy for children to choke on, so keep them away from under-fives. There's no problem if they're ground up, though. If there's any sign of mould on the nuts or shells, throw the whole bag away since it may carry a poison called aflotoxin.

It would be nice if we all had time to cook everything fresh, or had someone else to supply us with home-made dishes every day. But most of us are glad to have fast foods handy now and then. We know they're not a particularly healthy part of our diet – they just fill a gap. Some are better than others, and some are best kept away from small children. E numbers have such a bad name that it's easy to forget some of them are useful: added vitamins, for example, and certain preservatives, but most additives just add flavour or colour. Harmful bacteria have often been found in ready-cooked items, such as meats from a shop's chilled cabinet. Though healthy adults may not come to any harm, small children shouldn't be given this kind of meat since their immune systems aren't yet fully developed.

Children's immature immune systems make them more vulnerable to food poisoning than adults, so you need to be careful with dairy products. Eggs are often contaminated with bacteria including salmonella, so they should be cooked till both the yolk and the white are solid. Small children shouldn't be given cheese made from goat's or ewe's milk, or with an edible crust (like Camembert), because there's a small chance of listeria infection. Ewe's milk is also used in some forms of yoghurt, but it should be safe for children if it's pasteurised. The same goes for goat's milk, which is often recommended to replace cow's milk.

IMPORTANT POINTS

- Get children into the habit of washing their hands before they eat anything.
- If they're away from home and eating food with their hands, like burgers, they should use the paper napkin that's usually provided to hold the food.
- Because food poisoning is more dangerous to children, they should avoid anything made with unpasteurised milk or undercooked eggs.

HEALTHY OPTIONS

Important though it is to ensure our children don't eat contaminated food, that's not the most serious danger on their plates. The main problem with most children's diets is the amount of junk food eaten. Packed with saturated fat, salt and sugar, it fills them

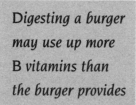

Digesting a burger may use up more B vitamins than the burger provides

up but provides little nourishment. In fact, digesting a burger may use up more B vitamins than the burger provides.

A healthy diet is important at any age, but never more than in childhood. That's when our bodies are growing fastest, incorporating everything we put into them, for good or bad. The way we eat then sets us on the path to lifelong health and energy, or to endless niggling health problems and low-level unwellness. Children, more than anyone, need to eat plenty of fruit and vegetables (frozen is fine if they're horrified by the sight of fresh veg). They need meat and dairy products or suitable body-building alternatives such as Quorn or other vegetable proteins. Bread and cereals are healthy fillers.

Like adults, children need to eat a wide range of foods to make sure they get all the nutrients they need, but most kids' diets contain little variety, despite all the different products. Read the labels on the sweets and munchies they fill up on and you'll see the same few ingredients again and again – mainly unhealthy or unnecessary, like sugar and additives. The more junk food they eat, the more restricted their diet really is.

Parents have a harder time now than even thirty years ago, when the range of junk food now available simply didn't exist. Then children ate real food or nothing. Now, it's hard to battle against the advertisers, who are allowed so much more time on children's television here than in most of Europe. And it's heartbreaking when meals turn into a battle of wills between parents and children. But the effort put into helping children build good eating habits is repaid many times over.

It's not surprising doctors have found children suffering from scurvy – a lethal but almost-forgotten disease that's easily cured with vitamin C – when many eat no fruit or veg other than chips. And resilient though children are, a bad diet in childhood can store up trouble for later life. Heart disease, for example, is linked with poor diet in childhood. Another frightening long-term result of this, or any form of malnutrition, is the brittle-bone disease osteoporosis which causes so much pain and injury in elderly people, especially women. The disease sets in when the bones begin to thin, so if young people don't build strong bones they risk suffering from it much earlier.

Milk is an important source of calcium, though ordinary cow's milk is not for babies as it can cause allergies. Children from one to five should drink full-fat milk, and semi-skimmed is all right for schoolchildren.

Children from one to five should drink full-fat milk

Switching to skimmed milk and low-fat cheese can placate a weight-watching teenager without losing any of the calcium content.

Most children like fruit juice, a powerful source of vitamins. But beware of 'fruit drinks' which tend to be sugar-laden and low in juice. And healthy though real juice is, it's best diluted to avoid tooth decay. Whole fruit is even better than fruit juice. In general, the less processed a food is – the less that's been done to it since it grew or walked around – the better it is for you.

Make sure, too, that children don't drink enough to ruin their appetites. Even milk and fruit juice don't contain all the nutrients they need, but soft drinks just rot their teeth and fill them up without providing any goodness at all. In fact, a lot of soft drinks have been found to contain more than the legal limit of artificial sweeteners, often together with sugar.

You may not have much control over what your children eat during the day, but breakfast is one meal that makes a lot of difference. Kids who eat a good breakfast do better at school because they can concentrate. It's worth waking them up early enough to have some healthy cereal like corn flakes, Weetabix or porridge, or wholemeal toast and fruit juice, or yoghurt with fresh fruit. Read the labels on cereals aimed at children, since these are often sugary junk food themselves – though still better than nothing in the mornings. You can often fool kids into eating healthier fare by sweetening ordinary cereals or yoghurt with a handful of dried fruit.

You can also help them do well at school by giving them lunches or snacks that will keep them going all day. Sandwiches are the great standby, especially if you use wholemeal bread: cheese or ham with salad are a good meal in themselves, with an apple or a banana. School meals used to be a mainstay of healthy diets until nutritional standards were abolished in the early eighties, which then allowed schools to serve any kind of junk as long as it was cheap. Thankfully new regulations should tighten up on that, but it's still worth providing food that you know is good rather than money that's more likely to go on sweets.

The odd bar of chocolate or bag of crisps won't matter as long as children eat plenty of fresh vegetables, whole grains, fruit and dairy products, with some meat or other protein foods. There's no need to worry if a child turns vegetar-

> **No *need to worry if a child turns vegetarian***

ian – just make sure they replace the meat with nuts, seeds, beans, pulses, eggs, cheese, tofu (made from soy beans) or meat substitutes like Quorn. If they turn strictly vegan, refusing even eggs or dairy products, consider giving them a vitamin B-complex supplement.

Watch out that you don't go to the other extreme, though, of putting your children on a diet that's not appropriate for their age. Though skimmed milk is recommended for adults to help keep our ever-increasing fat intake down, it's unsuitable for children. Children need slightly more fat (from healthy sources like dairy food and vegetable oils), because that's the most concentrated source of the calories they need for growing. Too much fibre fills them up so they can't take enough calories on board. In fact doctors have identified a new problem among children on the same low-fat diets their parents religiously follow – it's known as 'muesli-belt malnutrition'.

IMPORTANT POINTS

- Keep healthy snacks like fruit ready in the fridge. A banana is an excellent fast food.
- Get children up in time to have breakfast and to take a packed lunch.
- If they are overweight, just cut down on junk foods, get them to fill up with healthier meals, and join in new activities with them.

HYPERACTIVITY

Are children really more difficult than in the past? Judging from the number of prescriptions for mood-controlling drugs being dished out by doctors, maybe they are. More than a million children in the USA are prescribed amphetamine-type drugs like ritalin, which apparently help hyperactive children to concentrate. And the number of prescriptions is increasing here too. But are strong drugs the best way of dealing with this growing problem? Many parents are convinced that their children's

> *More than a million children in the USA are prescribed amphetamine-type drugs like ritalin*

problems stem from the vast number of chemicals – colourings, flavourings, preservatives – added to most of the food they eat.

At first they could only back this up with their own experience, such as children going berserk after eating colourful sweets, then medical evidence weighed in to support them. One large study of hyperactive children was published in The Lancet in 1985. It found that these children were more likely to react badly to food additives than to anything else. Benzoic acid (preservative E210) and tartrazine (yellow food colouring E102) had a bad effect on nearly eight out of ten of the children involved.

But it wasn't just additives that affected these children. Many were affected by ordinary foods too. Cow's milk and chocolate affected more than half. More than a third reacted to grapes, wheat, oranges, cheese and eggs, with peanuts and maize coming next on the list. Most of the children in this study also suffered other symptoms such as rashes, stomach ache and headaches and these also improved when they cut out the foods that made them hyperactive. So it looks as if additives are one problem, and food intolerance or allergy could be another.

The study was carried out very carefully, starting with an

exclusion diet on which the child ate a very small number of plain foods and gradually added one new food at a time. To rule out any psychological effect, the children and their parents didn't always know what they were eating. They might be given capsules, or a dish made with goat's milk instead of cow's milk. Additives E210 and E102 aren't the only culprits, though: other additives weren't tested in the study, and all the children who reacted to E210 and E102 also reacted to some other substances.

Cutting out danger foods is not the only answer. Though eighty-two per cent of the children improved when they no longer ate the foods they reacted to, only twenty-seven per cent made a full recovery. Did that mean they were still being affected by substances that hadn't been tested, such as other additives? Or did their behavioural problems have other causes too?

Of course children do behave badly for other reasons than food. They could be unhappy at home or school, or feeling insecure for other reasons. Brain damage, caused in the womb or during a difficult birth, can be subtle enough to affect behaviour when nothing else seems wrong. Many different chemicals can affect a baby's brain development in the womb. Women who smoke, drink or take drugs during pregnancy are more likely to have hyperactive children. This condition has also been linked with eating fish from polluted waters and even with tinned food during pregnancy. Hyperactivity has also been linked with children having a high intake of lead, through living near main roads and breathing in traffic fumes, or having old lead water pipes in the house.

Enough parents can pin their children's tantrums on what they've just eaten to make it worth looking at possible danger foods. Even if children have a tendency to hyperactivity, it seems they may be helped by avoiding the foods that are likely to trigger an attack.

American medical researchers have found that agitated people became calmer if they ate more food containing magnesium, selenium and chromium and less sugar. Children shouldn't be given vitamin or mineral supplements except in special children's formulations, but hyperactive kids might benefit from eating more wholemeal bread, Marmite (or other forms of brewer's yeast), leafy green vegetables, beans, onions, apricots, bananas and grapes.

Even more serious health problems can be linked with food. Some children suffering from autism, the brain condition that makes it hard for them to relate to people (remember Dustin Hoffman in *Rain Man*?), improve if they cut out a list of foods including cheese, chocolate, oranges, yeast, grapes and raspberries.

IMPORTANT POINTS

- These additives are the ones most often linked with behavioural problems in children: E102, E104, E107, E110, E120, E122, E123, E124, E127, E128, E131, E132, E133, E150, E151, E154, E155, E160b, E210, E211, E220, E250, E251, E320, E321.
- Cut down on brightly coloured or highly sweetened foods and snacks, especially sweets and soft drinks.

CHAPTER SIX

Safe eating on holiday

*S*tomach bugs are the biggest problem for travellers. They're not usually serious, but you don't want them to wipe out several days of your hard-earned holiday. In western Europe and the English-speaking countries, you'd be unlucky to encounter anything worse than an attack of food poisoning, leading to vomiting and diarrhoea. But if you venture further afield, you can meet nastier diseases. Occasionally you can pick up something that won't run its course in a few days, such as parasites, that can lead to long-term problems.

As world travel becomes more popular, we're starting to think of places like Kenya, Thailand and Turkey as regular holiday spots. Developing countries like these are exciting to visit because they are so unlike home, but together with beautiful scenery and fascinating cultures, the differences tend to include shorter life expectancy, poor health care and inadequate sanitation. The last thing travel agents mention is that the exotic destinations in their brochures may be rife with diseases that westerners never normally encounter, even though these kill a number of tourists every year. Kenya, for example, is a hotbed of malaria, yet you'd be unlikely to hear this from your travel consultant.

Cooks are no lazier in other countries than here, but the food and water they're working with may be less clean. Also, people tend to have some immunity to the bugs that surround them in their everyday lives. Away from home, coming in contact with new viruses and bacteria, we fall ill far more easily because we haven't had a chance to build up our resistance.

In years of travelling around the world, I rarely suffered food poisoning. One bout that stays in my mind happened after leaving a little inn in Kashmir. All the beauty of the stunning landscape was lost on me as I lay groaning on the seat of a bus winding its way further up into the mountains. I hadn't even seen the cheery cook waving goodbye while she washed up in an open sewer running past the kitchen, just downstream from someone using it as a lavatory – my travelling companion told me that later. This episode taught me that it's worth carrying your own cutlery around with you, making sure you wash it in clean hot water. True, the plates may be heaving with invisible bugs, but at least you're not putting them directly into your mouth (and using cutlery that may have come straight from someone else's mouth, too).

On the other hand, the second worst bout followed a meal in a very posh International hotel – a rare event on our travelling budget. That was where I learned that, in places where the electricity supply is unreliable, refrigeration causes delusions of safety. And expensive places with a small clientele have to keep food longer than cheap places where it gets used up fast.

Still, you don't have to venture off the beaten track to run into food hazards. In 1997 when the Consumers' Association researchers checked food outlets at thirteen British tourist attractions, they found more than half the sandwiches on sale contained high levels of bacteria and a fifth contained 'unsatisfactory' levels of food-poisoning bugs. And eggs from our very own battery farms are among the most dangerous in the world.

Keep in mind, too, that safe eating doesn't provide all the answers. Malaria, for example, the biggest killer, is spread by mosquitoes; it can be prevented only by taking tablets every day and avoiding mosquito bites. In fact, you should contact a specialist travel health centre at least two months before you plan to go, especially if you're travelling to any of the developing countries or if you're likely to venture outside tourist resorts. This allows time to organise a series of vaccinations or other precautions, like the anti-malaria tablets you need to start taking in advance of your trip. With the best will in the world, GPs are too busy with everyday illnesses to keep up to date with new hazards in other countries. Travel agents simply do not have the information, and have been known to give dangerously wrong advice.

Meanwhile, taking a few precautions with food and drink should protect you from the most common disorders.

WHAT TO DO

If you're holidaying in north-western Europe, North America, Australia or New Zealand, you only need to take the same precautions as you do when you're eating out at home. The advice that follows is more important the further you go from home. Sun-lovers heading for the tropics should be more cautious, bearing in mind that the food they're eating in an air-conditioned hotel started life in much poorer conditions and has been transported through the heat. Adventure travellers are most at risk, as they head into rural areas away from the tourist traps, but the main points apply anywhere. The safest food is hot, well done and freshly cooked.

> Safest food is hot, well done and freshly cooked

Cooking is important, since heat kills most of the dangerous organisms. As well as food poisoning and other food-borne diseases like hepatitis A, this includes the parasites commonly found in hot countries. Unlike travellers' diarrhoea, which usually comes and goes within a few days, parasites grow inside you until they're diagnosed and treated with drugs. A few very nasty ones may not be diagnosed until they have caused serious illness, and some can kill. Though we tend to be cautious about meat when we're travelling, it's just as important to ensure vegetables are well cooked too. They're not so likely to cause food poisoning but could easily carry parasite eggs or the hepatitis virus.

Human waste is often used to fertilise crops in developing countries – not a bad idea compared with our habit of flushing sewage into the sea and then smothering our crops with chemicals, but it does mean food needs to be very well cooked, which is how the local people usually eat it. That's where Western tourists tend to come unstuck. As soon as the heat hits us, we want to live on European-style salads and raw fruit.

Ironically, the very things we're always being told to eat for our health at home are the ones that are the likeliest to make us ill abroad. Salads and green, leafy vegetables, for example. Packed with vitamins, nothing could do you more good, but in any country where the produce is fertilised with 'night soil' (human excrement), this is the most likely food source to pass on disease: parasites as well as food poisoning. You can't peel them, and the leaves are nearly all surface area. Thoroughly washed, of course, they wouldn't be a problem – as long as you knew the water they were washed in was safe or boiled, but when you're not cooking food yourself you have little opportunity to check how hygienically it's prepared. And how many cooks are going to boil water, then let it cool down enough to wash the salad without wilting it?

Those holiday-makers who order chips with everything are making a wiser choice: peeled, plunged in boiling fat and served hot, chips are almost guaranteed free of bacteria. In fact, you're pretty safe with any vegetable

Chips are almost guaranteed free of bacteria

that can be peeled and is served hot and freshly cooked – even bread is safest, as well as most tempting, when it's fresh from the oven. Fruit is safe as long as you check that its skin is unbroken and peel it yourself. Watermelon is one exception, because it may have been injected with water to increase its size. Be careful, too, of fruits that can't be peeled: you need to be very sure of the water you wash them in. Unshelled nuts are a good bet, again as long as you see that the shells aren't broken and you can open them yourself.

Food-borne diseases are also spread by flies (which fly straight off excrement and on to the food you eat) or through simple lack of hygiene – when people don't wash their hands after using the loo.

What about those tempting little restaurants that offer the perfect end to a day in the sun? Trying local delicacies is half the fun of a holiday abroad, and there's no need to shy away from new tastes. Keeping to some simple rules will still allow you to sample a wide range of dishes. Look out for crowded restaurants, especially those that are crowded with

> *Local dishes are more likely to be correctly cooked than an attempt at Western cuisine*

local people rather than tourists – they know the best places to eat. Local dishes are more likely to be correctly cooked than an attempt at Western cuisine.

Many restaurants are happy for you to look in the kitchen, especially if the staff don't speak English and you can pantomime that you'd like to point to the things you want to eat. At the same time, you can sneak a quick look at the hygiene arrangements. Another clue is the loos: they're likely to be about as clean as the rest of the establishment. But if your sense of adventure takes you to some fascinating little dive where the cook looks like a mediaeval pirate and probably has the same standards of cleanliness, you can still reduce your risks by keeping to the following guidelines.

All meat and seafood should be served hot and well done. Don't eat it cold or raw. Apart from the food-poisoning risk, you could pick up a tapeworm from undercooked meat – not the sort of souvenir you want to bring back from holiday, though if you were really unlucky you might pick one up in Britain too. Beef tapeworms are the most dramatic, growing up to several metres long inside you (amazing how long our intestines are, all coiled up) but the ones you get from pork can spread through the body and cause lethal cysts in the brain. So it really is worth checking that meat is cooked all the way through, without a hint of redness. Snails too have to be very well cooked: those found in south-east Asia and the Pacific may carry a worm that causes a form of meningitis.

Seafood of all kinds seems to cause an inordinate amount of stomach trouble both at home and abroad. Shellfish in particular are famous for causing food poisoning or hepatitis, especially if they've been collected on polluted shores or from contaminated water. Even in this country they're a major source of stomach upsets. Some experts recommend not eating shellfish or prawns at all when you're travelling. Raw fish is probably safest in Japan, one of the cleanest countries you could visit, but even there it sometimes passes on parasites that would be killed by cooking. In the Pacific and Caribbean, fish are sometimes contaminated with the nerve poisons saxitoxin or ciguatoxin, either of which can prove fatal. This is a rare hazard, but if you feel ill after eating fish, do seek medical treatment at once.

If food is served with rice, make sure that is hot and freshly cooked. Bacillus cereus, the bug that thrives on warm grains, has been known to cause virulent bouts of Delhi Belly in travellers who prided themselves on being careful. A bed of rice is handy, though, if the plates look a bit dingy – just make sure you don't eat the bottom layer.

Even in north-western Europe and the English-speaking countries, where salad is a safe option, go for a vinaigrette dressing rather than mayonnaise. Vinegar has a slight antibacterial effect, whereas mayonnaise, containing raw egg, may be suspect. Eggs

> **Vinegar has a slight antibacterial effect**

are more dangerous in industrialised countries like ours than in Third World countries where chickens peck around in the dust.

Many books advise travellers to avoid street stalls and cheap restaurants but you're probably better off eating in a cheap and crowded workers' café, where there's a quick turnover of simple fresh food. The usual rules apply: hot food freshly cooked, and nothing raw unless you can peel it. There's no guarantee that staff in expensive hotels have more hygienic habits than anywhere else, and at least in the popular café food isn't likely to hang around long or be reheated. The same with street stalls. You just need to be sure that flies haven't walked over your food since it was cooked, which won't happen if you're shooing them away as you watch it cooking.

Even in the best hotels, be wary of buffets if you don't know how long the food has been standing out. The same goes for sauces and dressings that have been left out. They're probably harmless if the room is cool and there are no flies around, but you can't be sure what the conditions were like before you arrived. Expensive eateries are also more likely to cook very fancy dishes in which the food has been handled a lot and some ingredients may have been left cooling before they were

Be wary of buffets

added to the rest. As a basic rule of thumb, the fewer ingredients and the fewer steps in the recipe, the safer the dish.

The farther you get from the beaten track, the harder it will be to ensure that dairy products are pasteurised. Unpasteurised products carry the risk of diseases such as brucellosis, a 'flu-like disease which can last for years, and a form of tuberculosis that damages bones and joints. So it may be best to avoid any you're not sure of, including cheese and yoghurt. That also cuts out the risk of milk having been diluted with unsafe water. Tinned milk is fine.

Sadly, ice-cream and lollies can be risky if you're not in a clean-water area, since freezing doesn't kill all the bugs. Creamy desserts of any kind are a good breeding ground for bacteria.

Finally, don't let your safe eating intentions be sabotaged by the one person you thought you could rely on: yourself. Even at home, you should wash your hands both before preparing food and before eating. On holiday, it's twice as important. When you're out sight-seeing, you're likely to be picking up souvenirs in the market, feeling the embossed pattern on that fascinating old carving, pushing your dusty hair out of your face, slapping on another layer of sun-screen and leaving a sticky gloss on your hands for germs to settle in. Also, the loos may have been an experience you'd rather forget.

Your own hands may be the most dangerous thing that will touch your food. So be extra vigilant about washing them with soap and, if possible, hot water before you eat. If you have to pick up food in your fingers, leave the bit you've touched. In fact, even just touching your face can deposit germs near enough your nose and mouth to get in

IMPORTANT POINTS

- Food should be hot, well done, and freshly cooked.
- Peel all fruit yourself.
- Be wary of very complicated or Western-style dishes. The more ingredients and the more steps in the recipe, the greater the risk of food poisoning.

- Make sure your hands are clean before eating, especially if you're going to touch the food.
- Check with a specialist travel health centre – such as the Medical Advisory Service for Travellers Abroad or British Airways travel clinics (see Resources, page 137, 138) – whether you need vaccinations or other precautions. GPs and travel agents often don't have the latest information.

CAN I DRINK THE WATER?

Be careful of the local water supply when you're abroad, including popular spots like Greece and Turkey.

The best way to make water safe is to boil it. This will kill practically anything that could harm you. Best of all, filter the water first through a clean cloth or coffee filter to remove any sediment. Then let it boil for at least a minute (plus one extra minute for every 300m/1000ft you are above sea level) and store it in a clean container with a lid. This is easy to do in a hotel room, using one of those little plug-in water heaters that consist of an element on an electric lead. They're cheap and easily available from camping shops; the electric razor section of a department store will sell adapter plugs of the correct voltage for the country you're visiting. You can drink the water as soon as it's cool, or keep it overnight in a fridge if the electricity supply is reliable. If you're going somewhere very out of the way, where the water supply is really dubious and you can't boil it, you could take water-purifying tablets.

Given that most of us buy drinks when we're out, what's the best way to avoid trouble? The story goes that clean-living Katharine Hepburn fell ill through drinking local water while making The African Queen, while Humphrey Bogart and the rest of the film crew lived on whisky and stayed well. As long as they didn't mix it with water or ice, they probably would be safe from stomach bugs. Sadly, though, alcohol is one of the worst things to drink in hot climates, or when you're suffering from gippy tummy, since it makes you even more dehydrated (which in turn makes the hangovers worse.) Soft drinks are usually safe, especially if they're from one of the big international companies which exercise strict control over manufacturing. In developing countries bottles are often reused, but this is one time when recycling isn't such a brilliant idea since they may not be properly cleaned. Fizzy drinks are more likely to be the real thing; check the bottle top too, to see if it looks second-hand.

Hot drinks like tea are almost guaranteed safe, as long as you don't add unpasteurised milk. Take your tea the local way, neat or with sugar, or try drinking plain hot water – boiled, then allowed to cool a little – as

> **A *hot drink* can also be used to clean the rim of a cup**

people do in many countries to aid digestion. A hot drink can also be used to clean the rim of a cup, by pouring a little over the edge.

Also, remember, a lot of tourists live on Coca-Cola, religiously brush their teeth with bottled water, then fall prey to the one thing they hadn't thought of: the ice cubes in their drink. It's safer to have drinks straight from the fridge, or to chill the drink by standing it in ice.

Don't fall into the trap of not drinking – dehydration is more dangerous than most tummy bugs. We're constantly being advised to drink plenty of water, but few of us remember to keep topping up. Two litres a day is

> **Dehydration is more dangerous than most tummy bugs**

the World Health Organisation's advice, though few of us manage to swallow that much. Unfortunately tea, coffee and alcoholic drinks make you pass more water. We need even more fluid on holiday, when outdoor activities or hot weather sweat it off faster than ever. A water bottle is a good buy, to carry with you when you're out all day. Put it on your pre-holiday shopping list, though, rather than picking up an attractive goat-skin container at the local market: you never know what may be breeding inside.

Incidentally, if you wouldn't want to drink the water you'd be better off not swimming in it either. Some water can get into your mouth and nose while you're splashing around. And certain water-borne parasites don't need to be swallowed to find their way into your body.

IMPORTANT POINTS

- Boiled water is safest. In countries where tea is drunk warm, watch to see that the water for your tea has boiled.
- Well known brands of soft drink should be safe. Check the seal to see that the bottles haven't been refilled.
- Don't use ice cubes in unsafe water areas.
- Make sure you drink enough. If your urine turns darker yellow, you need to drink more water.

IF YOU DO FALL ILL

If a bout of diarrhoea lasts longer than a week or you're passing blood, send for a doctor. Diarrhoea can be dangerous if you lose too much fluid and become dehydrated. Signs of dehydration include dark yellow urine, dry tongue or loss of skin elasticity – for example if you pinch your stomach and the skin doesn't spring back in the normal way. If you stop passing urine altogether, or stop being able to drink, you need medical attention at once. You should also keep a close eye on children who fall ill, since it's easier for them to lose too much fluid and to become dangerously dehydrated.

Two of the most serious diseases spread by food or water are hepatitis A and typhoid. Hepatitis A is a viral liver infection that starts with a high temperature, loss of appetite, sickness, stomach pain, dark urine and a yellowish tinge to the skin and eyes. Typhoid begins like flu, with a headache, temperature, sore throat and sometimes diarrhoea. Both of these need prompt medical help. Safe eating can help prevent hepatitis A and typhoid, but it's worth being vaccinated against them if you're going to any area with poor sanitation. That can include rural areas and seaside resorts in Europe, as well as anywhere outside north-western Europe and the English-speaking countries.

But most cases of travellers' diarrhoea are over in two to three days and don't need treatment, especially since the remedies often have an uncomfortable constipating effect. Antibiotics hardly ever help and may even make matters worse. If you don't want to sit it out, take an over-the-counter remedy with you rather than having to try to find one while you're abroad and in the middle of an attack. Don't give anything containing loperamide to children under twelve; oral-rehydration therapy is the safe treatment for them.

It's worth taking some sachets of oral-rehydration solution with you, for adults as well as children to use after each trip to the loo during a bout of diarrhoea. Or make some for yourself by dissolving eight level teaspoonfuls of sugar or honey and half to one teaspoonful of salt in a litre of clean water. If you feel like taking the whole kit with you, you can add half a teaspoonful of baking soda and a pinch of cream of tartar to the mix as well, though these aren't vital.

The most important thing to do is keep your fluid levels up. Clean water is best, boiled if there's any doubt at all about its cleanliness. But soft drinks are often safer than the local water supply, which may have caused the trouble in the first place. If the worst comes to the worst, you're better off drinking bad water than none at all.

IMPORTANT POINTS

- The best treatment for travellers' diarrhoea and vomiting is oral-rehydration therapy (sugar and salt in water).
- Send for a doctor if you're ill for more than a week, if you're alone and losing strength or if you're passing blood.

TOXIC TREATS

Chocolate-coated ants, dog meat, witchety grubs – the thought of them might put you off, but intrepid travellers could try any of these without coming to grief. Some of the world's strangest recipes, though, include foods that are known to be poisonous.

The puffer fish, or fugu, is eaten as a delicacy in Japan, even though its roe, liver and skin contain a deadly nerve poison called tetrodotoxin, which kills about fifty per cent of those who swallow it. The fish has to be prepared by specially licensed chefs who carefully remove the dangerous parts. But that's still not foolproof and fugu kills several people every year. Enthusiasts say the heavenly taste is worth the risk; you may prefer to say heaven can wait.

The root vegetable cassava or manioc is the staple diet in many tropical countries, surprisingly, since it contains a form of cyanide and can kill if it's not correctly prepared. Every country where it's eaten has developed ways of removing the hydrocyanic acid, usually by soaking, boiling or pounding, so it isn't dangerous as long as it's prepared by a local person. Budget travellers shouldn't risk trying to cook it themselves, since mistakes are too dangerous to risk. Symptoms start with stomach pain and can progress to paralysis and death.

The same is true of ackee: don't try it at home unless you're sure what you're doing. Travellers to the Caribbean enjoy this strange fruit (B*lighia sapida*) that looks like scrambled eggs and is delicious served in the traditional way with salt fish. It is also popular in Nigeria, where it's called isin. Like cassava, this has to be carefully prepared to remove a naturally occurring poison that causes rapid lowering of blood sugar levels, followed by convulsions and death. The fruit has to be well boiled and the cooking water thrown away.

CHAPTER SEVEN

Safe supplementing

Year by year we eat less fresh food and take more vitamin pills. Do we really need all these food supplements? Doctors usually say they're unnecessary except in a few special cases, for example if you're pregnant or have a disease that stops you absorbing nutrients from food. But some researchers have found that our average intake of vital vitamins and minerals is lower than it should be. Doctors at the University of California got 500 volunteers aged nineteen to twenty-eight to write down what they ate each day and found they were most likely to be short of vitamins A, B6, C, D, E, folacin, magnesium, iron, zinc and calcium. It's not just down to being young and carefree: other American researchers studied a group of well-educated adults of all ages and found that their average intakes of calcium, iron, magnesium and zinc were below the recommended daily allowances (RDAs).

For most people, eating a healthier diet is the best answer. Good food helps the body fight off the harmful effects of stress, pollution and everything else modern life throws at it. The vitamins and minerals in food work together naturally to maximise their

Eating a healthier diet is the best answer

effects – vitamin C helps your body absorb iron and copper, for example. Sunshine on your skin is the best source of vitamin D, which helps the body absorb calcium for strong bones. Fruit and vegetables also contain hundreds of other compounds, any of which may do more good than the extracted vitamins.

There's not really much point taking supplements unless you think you're lacking some nutrient. How can you tell? Feeling tired for no apparent reason is one give-away sign, along with a tendency to catch every bug that's going around. If you're irritable or suffer badly from hormonal upsets like premenstrual syndrome (PMS), that can be a clue. Your skin is another indicator: a bad diet can leave it looking spotty or lifeless. If your doctor has ruled out any other health problems, it might be worth taking a multivitamin and multimineral supplement as well as trying to improve your diet. Give it three to six months – unless you're actually getting worse during this time – then if you haven't started noticing a definite improvement, go back to your GP. If other causes are still ruled out, you could ask to be referred to a state-registered dietician, who'll be able to find out if you're short of any vital nutrient.

Many alternative nutritionists think the official recommended daily amounts (RDAs) are too low. They may advise their clients to take large doses of one vitamin or mineral to try to treat diseases. This isn't a totally crazy idea – there's plenty of research showing that vitamin E, for example, may protect against heart disease and vitamin C can prevent a cold starting if you catch it in time. Iron cures one kind of anaemia and calcium keeps osteoporosis at bay. But our bodies work on a very delicate balance, which it's terribly easy to disturb by taking vitamin or mineral supplements, since they contain far more than you would get from food.

Unfortunately, while state-registered dieticians have a nationally recognised qualification and work in the National Health Service, the term 'nutritionist' can be used by anyone who likes the sound of it. Even letters after their name may just mean they've taken a short correspondence course. So if anyone other than a doctor or dietician advises you to take megadoses of a supplement, check with your doctor first.

AM I MISSING SOMETHING?

Even if you eat quite well, the ups and downs of everyday life leave you needing a bit extra sometimes.

Alcohol uses up zinc and magnesium

When you're under stress, for example, you need more vitamin B-complex and C.

If you're busier than usual, or doing a lot of exercise, you may need more zinc, iron, vitamins C, E and beta carotene.

Smokers need extra vitamin C, and alcohol uses up zinc and magnesium.

One in three teenaged girls is low in iron, a problem that goes on affecting a tenth of all women until the menopause.

Slimming diets are often short of all kinds of nutrients.

Vegetarians need to make sure they're getting enough calcium, iron, zinc and vitamin B12, and vegans, who don't eat any animal products (even eggs, milk or honey), need vitamin B12 supplements.

Eating a lot of meat, on the other hand, makes the body excrete more calcium.

The contraceptive pill reduces levels of vitamin B6, vitamin C and zinc.

Pregnancy and breastfeeding put a strain on the body while a lot of the goodness from your food goes to the baby – these are times when you need to eat more healthily than ever.

KEEPING THE BALANCE

Mineral levels are especially easy to unbalance. Taking very little more than the RDA of one mineral can cause a genuine deficiency of another. Even fairly small overdoses of mineral supplements have been known to kill children who get their hands on a bottle. Important though selenium is (and latest evidence suggests that a shortage may be linked with asthma) too much can be poisonous.

If you take iron tablets because you think you might be anaemic, they could stop you absorbing enough zinc and copper. So you add some zinc tablets to try to keep your immune system strong, but this reduces your iron and copper levels still further and leaves you short of calcium too. Quickly add a calcium supplement, to keep your bones strong, and your iron levels will soon be lower than ever. Just taking a higher dose doesn't help because our ability to absorb certain nutrients, such as iron, from supplements dwindles as the dose increases. You can end up swallowing pills till you rattle and feeling worse than ever – or even seriously affecting your health. And you may not realise you've depleted your resources of a vital mineral until the shortage makes you ill.

The safest way to take minerals is to stick to the RDA, and in a balanced supplement containing all the vital minerals.

Vitamin supplements also have their risks. The fat-soluble vitamins A, D, E and K, which are stored in your body instead of being excreted every day, are dangerous if they accumulate. An overdose of A can cause liver damage and birth defects; in fact it's best not to take vitamin A supplements at all since you get the same benefits from beta carotene without the risk. Overdoses of vitamin B6 may cause nerve damage. Too much vitamin E can interfere with the action of vitamin K and cause excessive bleeding. Even the ever-popular vitamin C can cause kidney stones if you're at risk of these – for example, if you have relatives who suffer from them – though drinking plenty of water may reduce the risk.

Kids who refuse to swallow cod-liver oil may be right: government research shows that fish-oil supplements frequently contain dioxins and PCB, two chemicals that have been linked with cancer and hormonal disorders. The problem stems from marine pollution and a daily dose could push children's intake of these harmful chemicals to the acceptable limit. Fish oils are rich in vitamin A, vitamin D and omega-3 fatty acids, but safer supplements like evening primrose oil go a long way towards providing the same benefits.

So don't take more than the RDA without expert advice. Vitamin C is the only general exception to this rule:

Don't take more than the RDA *without expert advice*

most people can get away with taking four or five grams a day to prevent a cold. But that's just for a few days; stop at once if you start suffering diarrhoea.

IF YOU TAKE SUPPLEMENTS

Most supplements last for up to nine months once the container is opened. Keep anything oily, such as capsules, in the fridge.

It's a good idea to divide supplements into several doses a day so that the effects last longer. You can reduce the risk of unbalancing your mineral levels, if you take a higher dose of one, by taking the higher dose supplement at one meal and a multimineral at another – as long as the combined dose is still within safe limits.

Taking supplements on an empty stomach can make you feel sick. Also, most supplements (especially fat-soluble vitamins) are absorbed better if you take them with food. Exceptions are vitamins B and C, which are absorbed just as well any time, and amino acids which should be taken half an hour before a meal. Horrible though they taste, calcium tablets have to be chewed up. If acidic vitamins like niacin and vitamin C upset your stomach, chew them well and take a bicarbonate tablet with them. Stop taking them if the problem persists.

If you have a reaction to a supplement, you could look for a hypoallergenic version. But there's no evidence that liquid or spray vitamins are more effective, and 'natural' ingredients are unlikely to work any better than others. Read the labels carefully: you may be swallowing wax, clay, sugar, lactose and artificial colours along with your nutrients. Capsules are safer; vegetarians should look for those made without gelatine. Big-name companies tend to have done more research. But there's no need to spend extra on above-RDA tablets unless you're sure you need them.

Occasionally, supplements have surprising side effects. Vitamin B3 makes your urine turn yellow, which is harmless, but it can also cause a skin rash, which may not be. If you have any odd effects, stop taking the tablets and see your doctor. If you don't feel any better, or more resistant to colds and bugs, within six months of starting to take supplements, you probably don't need them – unless you've been advised by an expert to take them as a preventative measure.

IMPORTANT POINTS

- Always check with your doctor before taking more than a recommended dose.
- Multivitamins and multiminerals are the safest, as long as they're balanced: check that they contain the RDA of each nutrient. In particular, it's safest to take the whole set of B vitamins together instead of just one.
- If you need medical treatment, tell your doctor you're taking supplements – they can interact with drugs.
- Take them regularly rather than stopping and starting, except when you're using vitamin C for a few days to blitz a cold. Except in emergencies, it's best to wean yourself off supplements rather than giving them up overnight, so your body has time to adjust to the change – people have been known to suffer 'rebound scurvy' when they stop taking megadoses of vitamin C.
- If you feel worse when you take supplements, stop taking them and see your doctor.

THE UPPER SAFE LEVELS (USL) FOR DAILY USE

If you do decide to take more than the recommended daily allowance of any vitamin or mineral, make sure you stay within these limits: anything higher could be harmful. Remember, though, that in taking a high dose of one nutrient you could fall short of others.

Measurements given by the Council for Responsible Nutrition, a supplement manufacturers' group, based on more than 300 scientific papers. RDAs are the European recommended daily allowances. Milligram (mg) = one thousandth of a gram; microgram (mcg) = one millionth of a gram.

Vitamin A	RDA 800mcg	USL 2,300mcg (800mcg for women who are pregnant or who may become pregnant)
Vitamin D	RDA 5mcg	USL 10mcg
Vitamin E	RDA 10mg	USL 800mg
Beta carotene	RDA n/a	USL 20mg
Thiamin (B1)	RDA 1.4mg	USL 100mg
Riboflavin (B2)	RDA 1.6mg	USL 200mg
{ Nicotinamide (B3)	RDA 18mg	USL 450mg }
{ Nicotinic acid (B3) do not take both	RDA 18mg	USL 150mg }
Vitamin B6 *new government recommendation 10mg maximum	RDA 2mg	USL 200mg *
Folic acid	RDA 200mcg	USL 400mcg
Vitamin B12	RDA 1mcg	USL 500mcg
Biotin	RDA 150mcg	USL 500mcg
Pantothenic acid	RDA 6mg	USL 500mg
Vitamin C	RDA 60mg	USL 2,000mg
Calcium	RDA 800mg	USL 1,500mg
Phosphorus	RDA 800mg	USL 1,500mg
Magnesium	RDA 300mg	USL 350mg
Copper	RDA n/a	USL 5mg
Chromium	RDA n/a	USL 200mcg
Iodine	RDA 150mcg	USL 500mcg
Iron	RDA 14mg	USL 15mg
Manganese	RDA n/a	USL 15mg
Molybdenum	RDA n/a	USL 200mcg
Selenium	RDA n/a	USL 200mcg
Zinc	RDA 15mg	USL 15mg

CHAPTER EIGHT

Food allergies
and intolerance

C ooking for company gets harder every year, as the number of people saying they're allergic to this or that continues to increase. You certainly wouldn't want to give someone the wrong food, because a true allergic reaction is frightening. Peanuts, for example, have become well known for causing anaphylactic shock, in which the victim's blood pressure drops sharply, their airways swell and they may lose consciousness and die. Less drastic reactions include wheezing, facial swelling, rashes, racing pulse and, of course, vomiting.

What makes this happen? It means something has confused your immune system, your body's defence against illness and infection. If you're allergic to, say, strawberries, your body thinks this harmless fruit is attacking it. Your immune system leaps to defend you, trying to expel the invader first by vomiting or diarrhoea, then by producing antibodies to it. Small blood vessels swell up, causing headaches, a blocked nose, and fluid retention. Muscles go into spasm, causing stomach pain and sometimes blocking the airways. You may get a runny nose as the body's secretions increase – all part of the attack on the invading organism. Some people are so allergic that the slightest taste of the offending food is enough to set them wheezing dangerously. In its worst form, anaphylactic shock can be triggered just by smell.

The numbers of people suffering from allergies is certainly rising. Peanut allergy is thought to affect one in seventy-five to eighty Britons, and kills five or six people every year in the UK. Anything up to forty per cent of the population believe they have some kind of allergy. But the official figure is still only about two per cent.

Why the difference? A true allergic reaction involves the immune system and has an effect within hours, often minutes. Far more people suffer (or believe they suffer) from food sensitivity or intolerance, causing less

> **A *true allergic* reaction involves the immune system**

dramatic reactions which may take place over the next few days. While allergies are easily diagnosed – both by the sufferer's obvious reaction and by skin or blood tests – food intolerances are much harder to pinpoint. Symptoms as vague as headaches, bloating, mood changes or just not feeling well don't really seem to be related to something you've eaten three days ago. In fact, many doctors don't believe food intolerance exists. They say things like headaches or

> **Food intolerances are much harder to pinpoint**

mood changes are just part of everyday life, not a reaction to an ordinary item of food. In some cases they suspect a kind of undercover anorexia – victims convincing themselves they're allergic to food that they're really frightened of, or they could be just plain hypochondriacs.

On the other hand, many people have benefited from giving up certain foods, especially wheat, yeast and dairy products. If the intolerance isn't to one of these common culprits, it can take quite a long time to track it down. Since the standard method is to give up all the foods that could be causing the problem, then to reintroduce them one by one, this shouldn't be done without medical supervision. It's easy to end up living on an unhealthily restricted diet. If you don't notice a really substantial difference within a few weeks, your problems probably aren't caused by food.

People who are allergic enough to suffer anaphylactic shock may need to carry a shot of adrenalin with them at all times, to stop an attack. In general, allergies can't be cured: you just have to try to avoid whatever triggers them and hope that in time they may wear off. Luckily, a lot of us do outgrow them, especially those that start in babyhood: at least one toddler in twenty suffers from allergies, but most have recovered before they reach the age of six. On the other hand, allergies can also start at any age, especially if you've been bingeing on one kind of food or drink.

In fact, one theory about the rise in the number of allergies over the past few decades is that we're all eating far more processed foods. Most of these contain small amounts of the same substances: soy beans, for example, and peanut oil. In the end our bodies rebel against these constant little doses. Most of us aren't affected, but be cautious if you have close relatives with asthma or eczema. These conditions are often linked with each other and with allergies, and people inherit a tendency to suffer all of them.

Outside factors also play a role. People can be allergic to many other things as well as food, and most of these allergies are caused by modern life. House dust mites find our centrally heated, carpeted, insulated homes as cosy as we do, which is partly why there's so much asthma around now. We use up our resources battling with pollution, not just from traffic fumes but from the many unexpected chemicals around our homes, such as formaldehyde in synthetic materials like carpets and furnishings; benzine from cigarettes, detergents and inks; and ozone from laser printers and photocopiers.

WHAT TO DO

Try to cut down on the amount of pollution your body has to deal with. It's not a guarantee of good health, but it makes sense to reduce the load, especially if you have a super-modern home full of chemical fumes, or live near a main road.

If you think you have an allergy, see your GP and ask to be referred to an allergy clinic. There you may be given a skin-prick test, which is when tiny amounts of common allergens are put into a series of little punctures in your skin, to see if there's a reaction within about fifteen minutes. Otherwise you can have blood tests, which are more complicated but may be able to pick up other allergies. You may be put on a strict exclusion diet, limiting you to a tiny number of specific foods and reintroducing the possible culprits one by one – time-consuming but very effective, especially where the reaction is more subtle than a rash or an asthma attack. Some specialists aim to cure allergies with the enyzme-potentiated desensitisation (EPD) treatment, which involves injecting allergens under the skin.

Food intolerances are more difficult to diagnose. Alternative practitioners have come up with all kinds of amazing machines and techniques that allegedly reveal hidden allergies and intolerances, but none of these have yet proved their worth in independent tests. They often advise cutting out a long list of foods, but this risks leaving you on an unhealthily restricted diet. As a rule of thumb, it's only worth excluding a food you like, or that's good for you, if you either lose the symptoms that were bothering you or feel substantially – not just slightly better within a month. If you have cut out something, like wheat or dairy products, that's part of a normal diet, make sure that you're replacing it with other nutritious foods. People with life-threatening allergies have to be certain of avoiding danger, but otherwise you're giving yourself more problems than you're solving if you become obsessive about 'wrong' foods.

If your symptoms are very vague, like just feeling moody or under the weather, and your GP has given you a clean bill of health, see if simple changes work before you start cutting out foods. Try eating a generally healthier diet, taking more exercise, getting out a bit more, or seeing if there are other problems in your life that need solving.

The National Society for Research into Allergy (see Resources, page 138) does a lot of work with allergies and other reactions that don't fit the usual medical model and can offer useful advice.

IMPORTANT POINTS

- No diet should cut out necessary food groups. If you go on an 'allergy' diet that cuts out many foods, check with a state-registered dietician that you're still getting the nutrients you need.
- Don't stay on a restrictive diet unless you notice significant improvements within two months.

THE CULPRITS

More than 160 foods have been proved to cause allergic reactions. But ninety per cent are caused by one of the following list:

Fish

Nuts

Peanuts (these aren't really nuts but are part of the same family as peas, beans and lentils)

Soy beans

Cow's milk products

Eggs

Crab and shellfish

Wheat

CHAPTER NINE

Long-term safety

You can't really look at safe eating without considering healthy eating. The difference is smaller than people tend to think. We're rightly concerned about the dangers of food poisoning and the contamination of our food supply, but we don't always think about the long-term damage wreaked by our own unhealthy eating patterns. Everyone knows that smoking causes lung cancer. It's not the only way to get lung cancer, just the most common one. How many of us know that a third of all cancers may be attributed to the food we eat?

The trouble is, most of the food we eat now is highly processed. That means it's had a lot done to it before it reaches our hands. Fresh fruit and vegetables and straightforward cuts of meat aren't processed, so we're in control of how they're cleaned and cooked. We can also see if they're not fresh. Anything in a tin or a packet, or already made or partly made, however, has been through a number of processes. These goods often require stabilisers and preservatives to keep them appearing the way they're meant to look. Their contents may be of lower quality than we'd choose for ourselves. We can't tell how much of, say, a burger or a fruit pie is made up of cheap filling agents, salt, fat, sugar, or even water.

An unexpected problem comes from the advice we're getting to cut down on fat. Yes, we do eat too much fat, and too much is bad for us but that's far from being the only unhealthy or unsafe element of our diets. 'Healthy eating' is a lot more positive than just cutting down on fat. After all, a lot of low-fat products are still pretty unwholesome, being packed with sugar or artificial sweeteners and processed to death. The emphasis on cutting down on fat gives manufacturers a chance to claim that over-processed foods, which are low in nutrition, are a healthy option just because some of the fat

'Healthy eating' is a lot more positive than just cutting down on fat

has been replaced by artificial sweeteners – which have a lot of safety question marks hanging over them. Even margarine, containing healthy vegetable oils, ends up being quite unwholesome thanks to all the processes it goes through.

Things are really turned on their heads when we're offered sugary soft drinks 'with added fibre' when fibre is freely available from ordinary fruit, vegetables and bread. Processed foods proclaim that they are 'low-fat' when fat is only a problem because of the amount of fatty processed food we eat. The 'healthy options' offered by the food industry are only healthier than most of its own unnourishing products, not healthier than the fresh minimally processed food we can easily make for ourselves.

A healthy diet includes protein, carbohydrates and some fat. Few of us are short of protein or fat, but most of us could do with more healthy carbohydrate in the form of fresh fruit and vegetables every day. The

A healthy diet includes protein, carbohydrates and some fat

basic World Health Organisation recommendation is five servings a day: a serving being one piece of fruit, or a handful of small fruit like raspberries, or an ordinary-size portion of vegetables on a plate. On average, we only eat two servings a day, so we could do ourselves a lot of good without going any further than the fruit bowl.

Frozen food is fine too. It often contains more vitamins than you'd find in fresh food that has travelled a long way since it was picked, though it doesn't have the texture of fresh food and no one's sure yet how the other nutrients hold up. Make sure you eat a wide range of foods in the course of a week – if you stick to the same few favourites you could be missing out on some nutrients.

If you like fizzy drinks, especially citrus flavours, buy them in bottles rather than cans. Alzheimer's Disease is thought to be connected with the amount of aluminium in our bodies, and fizzy drinks may contain some dissolved from the can. Don't have too many, though, even from bottles, since the carbonated drink can stop your body absorbing vital minerals, especially calcium, from food.

IMPORTANT POINTS

- Eat a lot more fresh fruit and vegetables. That's the most important change most of us could make to our diet.
- Cutting down on processed food automatically reduces your intake of saturated fat, salt, sugar, artificial sweeteners – all the things you don't need. It's also the easiest way of losing weight.
- The more processed a food is, the less control you have over what you're eating.

HOW MUCH DO I NEED?

To make use of the nutritional breakdown on a packet of food, you need to know how much of each item you should be eating every day. Don't become obsessed with this calculation, but it's useful to know if you're way out in some areas – and totting up your average daily intake can be surprising. Work out, too, if the information is 'per 100g' or 'per serving', then check if you get as many servings out of the packet as the manufacturer suggests. Their idea of a serving size is often smaller than ours!

Carbohydrates should be broken down into starches (which we need plenty of) and sugars (which we don't). The fat content can include healthy unsaturated fats, so the label should also show how much of it is saturated, the sort most of us need to cut down.

As a rule of thumb, the Consumers' Association advises that a product is high in fat if it has (for every 100g) 20g fat, high in sugar if it has 10g, high in saturates if it has 5g, high in sodium if it has 0.5g, and low in fibre if it has 0.5g or less. That doesn't mean you shouldn't eat products that don't fall within these categories as a treat. What the guidelines indicate is that they're not the best things on which to base your everyday menu. Healthy options – high in fibre and low in the substances we don't need so much – include up to 2g sugar, 3g fat, 1g saturates and 0.1g sodium per 100g, plus at least 3g fibre per 100g. Bear in mind these aren't the only considerations for good health: you also need to look at vitamins and minerals you need and check that the product isn't high in artificial sweeteners or any other additives you'd prefer to avoid.

ALL WE NEED EVERY DAY:

Sugars: men up to 70g, women up to 50g

Sodium: men up to 2.5g, women up to 2g

Total fat: men up to 95g, women up to 70g

Saturated fat: men up to 30g, women up to 20g

Dietary fibre: men at least 20g, women at least 16g.

THE DANGERS OF DIETING

Medical experts keep warning us that we're getting heavier by the year, and it's dangerously unhealthy. We miserably try to shed some weight and end up putting on more than ever. If only they'd come up with some foolproof way of getting in shape and staying there.

Well, they have. It's cheap, harmless and has no nasty side effects. But it's not 'new and improved'. It's the age-old good advice: get a bit more exercise and cut down on junk food. If only it were as easy to do as it is to say. Still, at least the weight you lose this way is likely to stay off, and any changes you've made are healthy ones that will do nothing but good.

Don't go on faddy diets. Eggs and grapefruit – or any other crazy combination – will wreak havoc in your intestines while leaving you short of energy and too weak to resist that bar of chocolate you can see floating before your eyes. Any weight you lose this way is likely to pile back on. Crash diets convince your body there's a famine on, so after the first shock it starts clinging to any fat it can keep on itself. Meal replacements are some of the worst things you could eat; usually they're nothing but confectionery with a few vitamins and fibre thrown in. They just reinforce the bad eating habits you want to break.

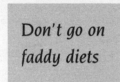

Don't go on faddy diets

IMPORTANT POINTS

- Instead of fretting about calorie-counts, try to cut down on processed food, fill up with more veg, and find a fun form of exercise you'll enjoy enough to do regularly.

CHAPTER TEN

What's up, Doc?

F ood poisoning can be caused by a number of different bacteria. Finding out what caused a bout of sickness can give you a clue as to where it came from, and how to avoid it in the future. If you do suffer from any of these, don't forget they may leave you exhausted for several weeks after.

UNSAFE BACTERIA

Bacillus cereus grows in leftover rice and occasionally in other cereal products such as pasta, or in stews and other meats. Sickness and stomach pains can come on within thirty minutes to eight hours; it may also cause diarrhoea within the next day. It only lasts a day or so but may leave you feeling exhausted for several more days.

Campylobacter jejuni is the most common form of food poisoning in Britain and is found in eggs, poultry, burgers or unpasteurised milk. It starts within a week, usually between three and five days after you ate the infected food. It causes headaches, nausea, abdominal pains and blood-stained diarrhoea, lasting three days to a week.

Clostridium botulinum, which causes botulism, is one of the world's most powerful poisons. It frequently ends in death; luckily it is virtually unheard of in this country. The toxin is destroyed by thorough cooking but can survive in tinned or home-preserved food – low-acid products like vegetables, mushrooms and meat paste – which hasn't been cooked for long enough at a high enough temperature. It has also been found in raw or smoked fish and a few other items. The symptoms of botulism can start in anything from four hours to seven days, usually within twelve to forty-eight hours. Unlike most forms of food poisoning it causes severe constipation instead of diarrhoea, plus dizziness, blurred vision, muscle weakness and difficulty breathing or swallowing. Seek medical help urgently if you have these symptoms.

Clostridium perfringens is found in cooked meats and other meals that have been kept warm too long. It comes on within eight to twenty-four hours, causing abdominal pains and diarrhoea, and is over within a couple of days.

Escherichia coli (E coli) is usually caused by food that is raw, under-cooked or inadequately reheated. It starts within six hours to three days, causing abdominal pain, high temperature and vomiting. If blood-stained diarrhoea starts, send for a doctor because it can then lead to kidney failure. It lasts up to a week, but kidney failure can happen even after the illness has eased off, so don't take it lightly.

Listeria monocytogenes usually takes about four days to incubate, though in some cases it has appeared several weeks after the infected food was eaten. It causes a high temperature, muscle pain and sometimes meningitis, a bacterial inflammation of the brain. It is carried by unpasteurised milk, mould-ripened soft cheese (such as Brie, Camembert or Vacherin), blue-veined cheeses, cook-chill chicken, badly kept meats, and unhygienically prepared or stored salads. Like salmonella, it should be over in a few days but you may not be fully recovered for several weeks. It can kill anyone old or weak and often causes miscarriage.

Salmonella can strike between six hours and three days after you ate the infected food, though it usually starts within twelve to thirty-six hours. It causes vomiting, diarrhoea, abdominal pains, heavy sweating and aching limbs. This can last from one to six days, but the sufferer may take several weeks to feel completely well again. It is usually carried in meat, poultry, milk or eggs – this includes products made from milk or those using uncooked eggs, such as mayonnaise. Cold meats and not-quite-cooked chicken are frequent culprits.

Staphylococcus aureus comes on within two to seven hours, causing abdominal pains, vomiting and sometimes diarrhoea. It's spread by cold meats, creams and custards or by unhygienic food handling – when someone in the kitchen has either sneezed over the food or has an uncovered septic cut on their finger. It lasts a couple of days.

Vibrio parahaemolyticus, from seafood, starts within forty-eight hours, causing stomach pain and cramps, watery diarrhoea and vomiting. It lasts two to three days.

WHO IS MOST AT RISK?

Anyone can develop food poisoning but healthy young adults are most likely to shake it off within a few days, unless they're unlucky enough to have something really dangerous like botulism. The main risk is to more vulnerable people, including children under two, old people, convalescents, pregnant women and anyone whose defences are weakened. This could be a result of illness, like AIDS or diabetes, or because they are taking drugs that suppress their immune system, such as those for cancer or after a transplant. Even antibiotics may reduce the body's ability to fight off illness.

If you're cooking for anyone in these groups, you need to take more care than ever about kitchen hygiene and checking that meat (especially poultry) is cooked through. People in these groups should avoid unpasteurised milk or anything made from it, especially soft mould-ripened cheese. Ordinary soft cheeses such as fromage frais or cream cheese are fine, but be wary of anything with a velvety white skin like Brie or Camembert, or with blue veins, like Danish Blue. It's also sensible to avoid soft-whip ice-cream from a machine, since fluctuating temperatures when the machine is turned on and off encourage the growth of any listeria that may be present. Fresh paté (even the vegetarian kind) and ready-to-eat chicken can be risky too; paté from a tin or jar should be kept in the fridge and used within two days.

Anything that might contain raw or lightly cooked egg carries a risk of salmonella, especially for vulnerable people. Eggs should be hard-boiled for at least seven minutes, or fried for three minutes each side, or scrambled till they're solid.

CHAPTER ELEVEN

Safe food production

F ood now is cheaper than it's ever been – or rather, the price we pay in shops is lower than ever (we pay millions of pounds every year in subsidies to farmers). Where sixty per cent of the average working household's income was spent on food in 1914 and thirty-five per cent in 1947, now it's just fourteen per cent. Modern food production has brought down the price of everyday items and allowed us to eat exotic food all year round.

The price we pay for this cheap food includes problems our grandparents couldn't have guessed at. Chicken, for instance, used to be a luxury; now factory farming means we can eat it every day of the week but we take the risk of food poisoning when we do. Like other meat, it may have been dosed on antibiotics and other drugs. When chickens were fed on grain and vegetable leftovers, we could eat them and their eggs without risking food poisoning. Mixing their food with drugs, feathers, animal scraps and their own excrement (yes, that goes in too) keeps the cost down. The same with other animals: crowding them into sheds and feeding them drugs, growth hormones and offal was cheap for the farmers but we paid the price. Growth hormones have now been banned from European farms, but they are still contained in meat from other countries and have been found, illegally, in some European products.

We no longer have to wait until fruit and vegetables are in season, but the chemicals used to ensure big crops all year round find their way into our water supplies, as well as directly on to our plates. When produce is brought in from abroad it could be full of even more dangerous chemicals that have already been banned here.

One problem we haven't even faced yet is the spread of harmful insects as pesticides kill off their natural predators. Dr Richard Lacey, the scientist who first said BSE could spread to human beings, has now warned that intensive farming methods are encouraging the spread of aphids – a problem the industry no longer dare meet with its usual answer of simply pouring on more pesticides.

In the rush to stay ahead, manufacturers use new products and processes without exhaustive safety testing. In other words, we're the guinea pigs. And we're also suffering the environmental effects of changed production methods. Much of the food we could grow here is imported, for example, with all the pollution caused by transporting it so far. Every ten litres of orange juice we buy has cost a litre of diesel fuel for processing and transport and 220 litres of water for irrigation and washing the fruit. Two thirds of the apples we eat come from abroad including New Zealand, Chile, South Africa and the USA. In France, ninety per cent of the apples sold are French, but in the UK only thirty-five per cent are home grown – we eat more French apples than English ones. Even at home, produce is driven around the country to giant warehouses then back again to supermarkets near where it was grown. Food is over-processed and sprayed with extra pesticides to survive the journeys and small farms are forced out of business, reducing our chances of buying locally.

We've also lost the variety of fruits and vegetables we used to have. That seems an odd claim, now that we can pick up rock-hard mangoes and tasteless avocados in any supermarket, but in fact the range of fruit and veg readily available to shoppers has plunged in the past fifty years. Who has ever tasted potato onions, pig's snout apples or hedgehog pears? We've lost

> *Every ten litres of orange juice we buy has cost a litre of diesel fuel for processing and transport*

thousands of old native varieties. A handful of multinational agrochemical companies own the patents for most of the produce now available. It's bred for convenience: standard shapes and sizes, ability to resist long journeys. The fact that so much of it is tasteless and mushy is irrelevant. It's wonderful that some supermarkets are now displaying tomatoes labelled 'grown for taste', as if that's the last thing you'd expect of them! A shift in attitude could mean all our produce was grown for taste and quality – and that will only come if we, the shoppers, demand it.

Could we choose healthier options now, even if we wanted to? An ever-increasing number of households has no one at work, so food takes up a much larger part of their small income. Local shops close down as an area becomes poorer, or survive by stocking processed food that keeps longer than fresh produce. If safer food meant higher prices, these families would be hit even harder.

Those of us who do have jobs are working longer hours to keep them. We feel we don't have time to shop and cook. We trek to the edge of town to stock up at hypermarkets. That's not a journey you'd want to do every few days, and we're too busy anyway, so we shop less often. That means we either have to buy processed food full of preservatives, or risk storing food longer than is really safe. Freezers seem like the answer. But our hectic lives mean we don't always have time to let food defrost properly – a major food-poisoning risk.

Part of the solution to both problems is to shop locally. Hypermarkets can easily bankrupt high street shops and supermarkets, then put their prices up as they wipe out any competition. The more of us using our local shops, the more they'll flourish, expanding their ranges and keeping their prices down. They're handy enough to visit more often and you don't need a car.

Shop locally

On top of that, most of our food safety problems have been caused by changes in the law or by food suppliers. But we're not helpless. The implanting of growth hormones in cattle was finally banned from the EC in 1986 after a long campaign by ordinary people, despite our government's efforts to prevent the ban. The US government, again backed by ours, has lobbied to have the ban dropped so American companies can sell a new growth hormone called BST. So the campaign is on again.

IMPORTANT POINT

- Every time we win an improvement in food safety, it's because enough people have let shops, manufacturers and their MPs know it matters.

THE MAD COW STORY

The story of the bovine spongiform encephalopathy (BSE) epidemic is the story of what's gone wrong with British farming, in a nutshell. It includes examples of practically everything food safety campaigners complain about.

Animal welfare groups were the first to campaign against factory farming, on the grounds of cruelty to animals, but they were easy to write off as cranks and

Campaign against factory farming

do-gooders. It was some time before the consequences to human health became obvious.

Controls on the use of animal scraps in cattle feed were relaxed in 1981, as part of the government bonfire of so-called 'red tape' – in other words, life-saving health and safety regulations. The bodies of sheep (some with a brain disease called scrapie) were already being minced up and used as cattle fodder. Cattle are vegetarian, naturally living on grass. But this nasty mix was cheap and convenient. The fatal change in 1981 was a relaxing of controls over the heat at which this mix had to be cooked to make it sterile.

Also during the eighties, farmers in certain parts of the country were compelled by law to drench animals with organophosphates, originally developed for military use as nerve gas. This was intended to eradicate warble fly, a pest that causes discoloration of cow hide. Opponents protested that this was using a sledgehammer to crack a nut: it was dangerous to the cattle, and not justified by the small nuisance caused by warble fly. Organo-phosphates have also been strongly linked with nerve damage in farm workers. These protests were ignored. No one has proved that organophosphates contributed to the spread of BSE but one theory is that by weakening the cattle's immune systems, it reduced their resistance to the disease.

The first signs of this new disease were seen in 1985, when a Kent farmer saw his cows staggering and falling down. They eventually became demented, giving rise to the name 'Mad Cow disease', and soon died. Microscope examination of their brains showed sponge-like changes. BSE was identified the following year. Incredibly, it wasn't until 1988 that the government declared it a notifiable disease, ordered all infected cattle to be destroyed and banned the use of their milk for any purpose except feeding their own calves. That year too, animal protein was banned from cattle feed (though not necessarily from the feed of other animals destined to be eaten).

Even in November 1989, after the BSE crisis, only certain parts of the offal of cattle over six months old were banned from use in human food (the spinal cord, brain, intestine, thymus gland and tonsils). It was only in 1994 that the thymus gland and intestines of calves under six months were added to the ban. Late in 1997 the government took the further step of banning beef on the bone from sale after a report suggested that the disease might be found in bone marrow.

By June 1997, while thousands of cows were still being incinerated, there had been 169,349 confirmed cases of BSE in British cattle on more than 30,000 farms. Another 400 cases had been confirmed in Ireland and other parts of Europe. Thousands of British breeding cattle had been exported during the eighties, along with tonnes of bonemeal. And in some countries, they had been using the same kind of cattle feed. The crisis had cost a total of about £3,000 million to date in the UK alone.

More importantly, it had cost human lives. A new version of the degenerative illness Creuzfeldt-Jakob Disease (CJD) had started killing people, and most of its victims were young. Even those who had been vegetarian for more than a decade were not immune, since the disease could have been incubating since 1981. As late as 1996 the government was still claiming there was no proof that CJD was definitely caused by BSE. By the next year more than twenty were dead and no one knew how many more would fall ill.

BSE is a strange disease. It's passed on by a prion: an oddly shaped molecule that has the power to make

The strangest thing about BSE was how it was allowed to happen

other molecules take on the same shape, so they can't carry out their normal functions. Many people feel the strangest thing about BSE was how it was allowed to happen.

GENETIC MODIFICATION

This sounds like science fiction, but genetic modification or genetic engineering is already happening. Scientists are swapping genetic material from one species to another: fish genes into tomatoes, for example, and human genes into pigs. The idea is to

Genetic engineering is already happening

create new, improved versions. Supporters say it's just a quicker way of doing what farmers have always done, breeding for preferred characteristics. Opponents say you could work on tomatoes for ever and still not get them to interbreed with fish.

Genetically modified (GM) food slipped into our shops very quietly, without being labelled. At first it was a few products like the Flavr Savr tomatoes, that last longer and make a thicker paste, and a new ingredient in vegetarian cheese. (Normal cheese isn't vegetarian since it contains rennet, made from a calf's stomach; the new product increased production of the vegetable replacement.)

A company called Monsanto took things a step further by creating Roundup Ready soy beans, specifically developed to resist the company's pesticide, Roundup. Despite protests, Monsanto lobbied successfully for the GM beans to be mixed in with the rest of the soy bean crop, so consumers can't call for products containing the GM beans to be labelled. Since soy is used in about sixty per cent of processed foods, this means most of us have already eaten GM products without realising.

The trouble is, the genetic code is immensely complex. Scientists say they know exactly what they're doing, but no one yet knows all the consequences of putting genes from one species into another.

Many risks have already become clear. In 1989, a genetically altered form of the food supplement tryptophan caused a new disease called eosinophilia-myalgia syndrome that killed thirty-seven people in the USA and left 1500 others disabled. The company making the supplement had used genetic modification to speed up the process, without realising they had created a poison. BST, a genetically modified hormone that makes cows produce more milk, has been linked with intestinal cancer in human beings.

Other dangers can only be guessed at. A gene may behave differently when it is transferred to a different organism and could cause unpredictable changes in the host. New plants could increase out of control and damage the environment. Dangerous diseases could cross the species barrier, possibly becoming far more virulent in the process, and mutations of the genetic code could create new diseases. Genetically modified animals are already prone to all kinds of weakness and disease. Chickens created to resist salmonella, for example, turned out to be more vulnerable to cancer.

The long-term effects on people and the environment are unknown. In Canada, a gene for scorpion toxin has been inserted into an insect virus and used as an insecticide, despite fears that it could create a frightening new disease in humans. New forms of potato and corn actually contain pesticides, conveniently for the farmers who don't have to spray but unnerving for the people eating them. Though human stomach acid is said to neutralise the pesticide, there are fears that these foods may cause allergies or even poison people using ulcer drugs or antacids that reduce stomach acidity.

Organisations like the SAFE Alliance and the Food Commission are fighting for GM food to be labelled, so people can choose whether to buy it. At present you can only be certain of avoiding it by eating no non-organic processed foods – an unrealistic target for most of us. But supermarkets don't want to scare their customers away, so let yours know you don't want to buy GM food without being told.

THE ORGANIC ANSWER

By far the best solution to our safety concerns is organic food, produced under natural conditions without the use of chemicals. Organic vegetables and fruit are grown without artificial fertilisers or pesticides, in ground that has to be certified free of contamination. Organic products such as cakes or pies may contain a small percentage of non-organic ingredients, but these have to be shown on the label. Nothing that's labelled 'organic' has been irradiated or contains genetically modified organisms (GMOs).

Organic meat comes from animals kept under more natural conditions than those of factory farms. Instead of relying on the routine use of drugs (including antibiotics) to prevent diseases caused by stress and overcrowding, organic farmers keep animals in more comfortable surroundings. They are given drugs to cure disease only if gentler methods have failed to help. Even if an organic animal has been given medicine, the farmer must leave it twice as long as a conventional farmer does before slaughtering, reducing our risk of swallowing antibiotic residues. The animals live on drug-free natural foods and those that don't naturally eat meat aren't fed any animal protein. Animal products from organic suppliers are genuinely free-range, since the animals are allowed to wander outdoors instead of living their whole lives in indoor stalls or

Animal products from organic suppliers are genuinely free-range

cages with barely room to move. It's altogether a more humane way of keeping animals, as well as a healthier alternative for us.

Organic herds, for example, were largely safe from BSE because they were fed on natural foodstuffs such as corn and grass rather than on the remnants of animal carcasses. The Soil Association – the biggest organic farming group – banned the feeding of any animal material, including fish, to cattle or sheep in 1983. No BSE has been found in cattle born on organic farms that had been certified organic before 1985. The reason a few cases have been found in other organic herds is that farmers may have been changing over from conventional to organic farming, or non-organic cattle may have been bought to increase the herd size – those cattle wouldn't be called organic, but their calves would.

In some parts of the country, even organic farmers were compelled by law to use organophosphates on their cattle during the eighties, and those herds lost their organic status for the following year. Luckily these healthy and well-fed animals were strong enough to withstand the effects of organophosphates.

Organic food tends to cost a bit more, because its producers don't receive the massive subsidies that support intensive farming and because it's cheaper to keep animals indoors in crowded conditions. Of all the money spent on farming subsidies in Britain, only three per cent goes to support organic farming, with just 0.3 per cent of our land being organically farmed. This isn't a simple question of supply and demand: nearly three quarters of the organic food sold in our shops has to be imported. Other countries take it more seriously: in Austria, for example, ten per cent of farmland is organic.

The more chemicals you use, the more you need: intensive farming depletes the soil, creating a need for more fertiliser. Poisons are sprayed on crops to kill pests, but they make the problem worse by also killing many of the animals and insects that would otherwise have eaten the pests.

Supporters point out that organic farming is better for the environment as well as our health: the chemicals sprayed on crops find their way into our water supply after rain carries them into rivers. It also employs more people, since unsprayed crops need to be weeded and generally looked after. Orthodox farming relies on huge

Organic farming is better for the environment

areas of a single crop – monocultures – wiping out any other plants that might grow in the area, including natural hedgerow, the habitat for many of our fast-disappearing species of wildlife.

IMPORTANT POINTS

- Organic food does not contain chemical residues or genetically modified ingredients and it is not irradiated. If the US government wins its battle to overturn European law banning the use of growth hormones, organic meat will be the only kind guaranteed hormone-free.
- If you can't afford to eat all organic food, concentrate on meat, eggs and root vegetables. These are the most damaged by intensive farming methods.
- Children are most the endangered by chemical residues, so organic food is more important for them.

HOW DO I KNOW IT'S ORGANIC?

The production and importing of organic food is strictly controlled by the government, through six approved organisations reporting to the United Kingdom Register of Organic Food Standards (UKROFS). These are the Soil Association Organic Marketing Company; the Biodynamic Agricultural Association; Organic Farmers and Growers Ltd; the Organic Food Federation; the Scottish Organic Producers Association; and the Irish Organic Farmers and Growers Association. Food bearing any one of their symbols is certified organic. All organic products should have one of these symbols on their packaging.

Farmers, manufacturers and importers all have to meet EC regulations covering organic production and are regularly inspected. These cover a number of areas as well as animal health and welfare. They ensure that no non-approved fertilisers or pesticides have been used, appropriate crop rotation has been practised and correct measures

> **No non-approved fertilisers or pesticides have been used**

have been taken to protect the environment, including wildlife habitats. Land has to be farmed organically for two years to clean the soil of chemicals from previous use before produce grown there can be sold as organic. Animals that have been given medicine can't be sold for meat until after the drugs have cleared from their bodies.

It would be useful if the approved symbols were displayed on all organic food, but unfortunately you won't find individual stickers on pieces of fruit or joints of meat. Shops usually label their organic produce shelves separately from the rest. You have to take this on trust, but there are stringent penalties for claiming food is organic when it is not. If you suspect food being sold as organic, for example in a market, is really conventional produce with a big mark-up, contact your local council's trading standards department who can send someone to do a spot-check.

WHERE CAN I BUY ORGANIC FOOD?

As people grow more concerned about food safety, organic produce is becoming more widely available. You can even ensure healthier hangovers by buying organic wine and beer. It's worth asking your local shops if they'll consider stocking organic food, or contact the Soil Association for a list of suppliers. With supermarkets reporting, late in 1997, that the demand for organic food had doubled in just two years, availability is improving all the time.

In general, dairy products (including eggs) are the most frequently stocked organic foods in supermarkets. You may have to scout around more for other things like fruit and veg, cereals, meat, baby foods and alcohol. Organic meat, unfortunately, is harder to find in supermarkets: at present only selected branches of Safeway, Sainsbury's, Tesco and Waitrose sell it.

Among the big chains, Safeway and Sainsbury's are the best suppliers at present, with all kinds of organics widely available. Waitrose and Tesco stock them all in at least some branches and are committed to expanding. The Co-op has most kinds of organic food in at least some of its branches.

You should find dairy produce in all Asdas and some Somerfields, though these two chains don't stock any other organic food. Asda shoppers could try writing to ask for more, since head office is open to suggestions on the company's organic policy. Surprisingly, upmarket Marks & Spencer doesn't stock organic food at all, having tried it unsuccessfully a few years ago. They are reconsidering this policy at the moment, though, so you may soon be able to pick up some organic yoghurt when you pop in for a pair of tights.

Many independent shops offer a wider range, including wholefood and health food stores and some butchers. Specialist shops are cropping up all over the country, including two organic supermarket chains: Out of This World has branches in Bristol, Newcastle-upon-Tyne and Nottingham, and Planet Organic is planning to expand from its London base.

The Soil Association's book, *Where to Buy Organic Food*, lists hundreds of outlets around the UK. As well as the ever-growing number of shops, these include farms that sell directly to the public, markets, mail-order companies and box schemes. These last two are a boon for anyone who doesn't have a good organic shop close to home.

No matter where you live, a whole range of organic products can be delivered to

Where to Buy Organic Food *lists hundreds of outlets*

your doorstep. At the last count there were seventy-seven organic mail-order suppliers covering the whole UK – and practically everything you could ever

Seventy-seven organic mail-order suppliers cover the whole UK

want to eat (including organic chocolate). On top of that, you can choose from cosmetics, baby foods, Christmas hampers, seeds to plant in your own vegetable patch, essential oils and any kind of drink from fine wine to scrumpy.

Box schemes are a particularly welcome new development, since they make life easier as well as ensuring food safety. You join a scheme operating in your area – they are becoming so popular that you may have several to choose from – then instead of trekking round the supermarket and lugging bags of shopping home, you simply order the goods and wait for them to be delivered.

Before you think of the obvious downside – they must cost a fortune – box schemes are not necessarily an expensive alternative. Prices vary, and many offer better value than supermarkets. We're used

Box schemes are not necessarily an expensive alternative

to home deliveries being a luxury, but they were an everyday convenience to our grandparents. It makes sense, after all: suppliers don't have the overheads of running a shop and may keep transport costs low by supplying to all their customers in one area on the same day. Some schemes deliver on set days and at certain times, while others are more flexible about coming when you're at home.

Fruit and vegetables are the basic fare, but many also offer meat, eggs and cheese, while some have a range of other products too. To avoid wastage and to keep expenses down even further, some suppliers offer a set-price box, say for £10, containing a selection of the fruit or vegetables available on that day. You can express general preferences and say if there's anything you don't want, but you won't have chosen each item individually. Others send out price lists and you simply order the goods you want: a pound of this, a jar of that, half a dozen of those. It couldn't be easier.

Some box schemes are operated by individual organic growers, others by companies that buy the produce in. You may have the chance to invest in the farm as part of an expansion project. If you're on a tight budget, you may even be able to do some work in return for food. Contact the Soil Association (see Resources) to find what's available in your area.

Organic food in the supermarkets

	Fruit & vegetables	Cereal products	Dairy products	Meat	Baby food	Wine & beer
Asda	✗	✗	✓✓✓	✗	✗	✗
Co-op	✓	✓	✓	✗	✓	✓
Safeway ¹	✓✓	✓✓	✓✓✓	✓	✓✓	✓
Sainsbury	✓✓	✓✓	✓✓✓	✓	✓✓	✓
Somerfield	✗	✗	✓	✗	✗	✗
Tesco	✓✓	✓✓	✓✓	✓	✓	✓
M&S	✗	✗	✗	✗	✗	✗
Waitrose	✓✓	✓✓	✓✓	✓	✓✓	✓✓

Table compiled using information received from the Soil Association

Key: ✓✓✓= all stores   ✓✓= most stores   ✓= some stores   ✗= not stocked

¹ = first supermarket to stock organic produce

CHAPTER TWELVE

New and improved?

DEREGULATION

Abolishing or relaxing regulations in the name of 'cutting red tape' was a theme of the 1980s. It allowed farmers to feed cattle unsterilised animal protein, for example, and it let education authorities drop all the nutritional standards for school meals.

Benefits
Saves money – though not for the consumer.

Dangers
Loss of health and safety legislation and consumer protection.

Solutions
Individual: there's not much we can do except be vigilant.

The big picture: reintroduction and stringent policing of safety controls over farmers and food suppliers.

GENETIC MODIFICATION

A new process that swaps genes from one species to another: fish genes into fruit, for example, and human genes into pigs. We are already eating genetically modified (GM) food.

Benefits
Theoretically the sky's the limit: science could create baked beans that healed brain tumours. At present it is mainly convenient to manufacturers, for example giving products longer shelf life.

Dangers

Long-term effects are unknown, but many problems have already occurred (pp 118-9)

Solutions

Individual: buy from shops or manufacturers that have stated they will not use GM products, or will clearly label products if they have. Buy organic food where possible, since legally it has to be free of GM ingredients.

The big picture: government action is needed. Meanwhile, campaign for honest labelling; tell food manufacturers and your supermarket that you want to know what you're buying. Write and ask your MP to support this.

IRRADIATION

Fruit and vegetables are hit with quick blast of radiation, to halt signs of ageing in their tracks.

Benefits

Slows down the decay of fruit and veg.

Dangers

Vitamin content of the produce diminishes with age: irradiation allows old food to be sold as if it's fresh. Long-term effects of eating irradiated food are unknown.

Solutions

Individual: buy organic produce, since this is not allowed to be irradiated.

The big picture: let your supermarket know you don't want to buy irradiated produce. The introduction of safety controls over farmers and food suppliers is needed, and tighter enforcement of import laws that currently let irradiated food into the country.

MICROWAVE OVENS

This speedy new cooking process has won friends among busy cooks.

Benefits
Shorter cooking times. May preserve more vitamins in vegetables.

Dangers
Food may not be properly cooked all the way through. It is not yet known whether microwaves give out harmful radiation.

Solutions
Individually: follow the instructions to the letter, but also check by cutting into meat to see that it's well done. Keep away from a microwave when it's in use and never use one with a damaged door or seal.

The big picture: keep your eyes open for the latest research reported in the press.

CHEMICALS IN FOOD

Before the Second World War, farmers used very few chemicals. Since then these have become the mainstay of food production. Now the independent Advisory Committee on Pesticides finds 'higher than desirable levels' of residues in some fruit on sale – the latest in a series of similar official findings. In 1995, forty-six per cent of fruit and veg tested was found to contain residues. Chemical fertilisers may also be harmful.

Benefits
Bigger crops.

Dangers
Pesticides are poisons. Their residues are known to cause symptoms including stomach pains and vomiting; pesticides are suspected of causing a series of other conditions, including nerve damage and cancer.

Solutions

Individually: wash and peel fruit and veg; where possible, buy from organic suppliers (none use chemicals).

The big picture: changes in farming practice are needed. Subsidies could be given to help farmers go organic, instead of paying them to leave land unused or supporting intensive farming.

ROUTINE MEDICATION

Animals raised for meat are routinely dosed with a string of medicines, including antibiotics.

Benefits

Prevents diseases largely caused by overcrowding and bad conditions.

Dangers

Overuse of antibiotics causes development of antibiotic-resistant bacteria, affecting humans as well as animals. Other side-effects are possible and drug residues have been found in the meat we eat. Long-term effects unknown.

Solutions

Individually: eat organic meat.

The big picture: changes in farming practice. Britain has to accept and support EC safety regulations.

CENTRALISATION

Out-of-town hypermarkets replacing local shops.

Benefits

The ability to pick up all your shopping in one swoop. Huge shops can keep prices down and there's plenty of room to park.

Dangers

The closure of smaller shops reduces competition. Food becomes less accessible to people without cars. Buying less often means food is more likely to be stored for too long, or has to contain more preservatives.

Solutions

Individually: shop locally whenever you can.

The big picture: let your council know you don't want more hypermarkets when chains make planning applications.

FOOD MILES

Our food is imported from around the world. Food transport inside the UK has increased by an average fifty per cent since 1979 and imports have doubled in the same time.

Benefits

The supermarkets can set up bulk deals and buy slightly cheaper from abroad.

Dangers

Pollution from long-distance lorries and planes, waste of resources, over-processing of food and overuse of chemicals for the journey. Small local farms are forced out of business.

Solutions

Individually: look for locally grown produce by checking labels. If one is available, join a local farm's organic box scheme.

The big picture: let supermarket managers or head office know you want locally grown food. Don't be thrown by claims that it will cost more: we're all paying the price in pollution and job losses. At present seventy per cent of organic food has to be imported, so asking the government to support local organic farmers also helps to reduce food miles.

LAX FOOD-HANDLING PRACTICES

By suppliers, slaughterers, shops and us in the kitchen! It's more of a problem now with food travelling greater distances and the people involved being far from where customers can keep an eye on them.

Benefits
Convenience.

Dangers
Food poisoning, which can be fatal. Other diseases can also be transferred by infected food coming into contact with clean food.

Solutions
Individually: safe shopping and food-preparation practices.
   The big picture: tighter controls on suppliers, slaughter-houses and shops, which are more rigorously enforced.

VITAMIN AND MINERAL SUPPLEMENTS

We take these in huge numbers, but in most cases the benefits haven't been proven.

Benefits
Could do you good, especially if you have a poor diet or suffer from an inability to absorb certain nutrients from food.

Dangers
It's easy to knock your vitamin and mineral levels out of balance. Taking very little more than the recommended daily allowance (RDA) of one mineral can cause a deficiency of another.

Solutions
Individual: don't exceed recommended doses without detailed

advice from doctor or reliable dietician. Don't take them at all if you don't need them.

WATER CONTAMINATION

This happens in two ways: there are big scares when some kind of bug gets into the water supply and customers are told to boil their water; a more everyday problem is the constant presence of unwanted chemicals in our water supply.

Benefits
Some chemicals, like fluoride, are added as a health measure. Lax hygiene measures save money for water companies.

Dangers
Chemicals found in domestic water may include pesticide and fertiliser residues as run-off from farmland and lead from old household pipes.

Solutions
Individual: get the council to check your pipes. Buy a water filter and change it regularly.

The big picture: tighter controls over both water suppliers and polluters – including manufacturers who dispose carelessly of waste products.

PROCESSED FOODS

Many of these look just like things our mothers made, but they contain very different ingredients.

Benefits
Quick, easy, versatile.

Dangers

It's easy to eat an all-processed diet without realising you're missing out on many nutrients. Also convenience foods use additives and processes (such as the hydrogenation of fats – the way that the structure of fat changes during the food manufacturing process) that have been linked with disorders including heart disease and some cancers.

Solutions

Individual: make sure you eat some fresh fruit and vegetables every day.

The big picture: an improvement in standards, to make processed foods more wholesome.

FOOD ALLERGIES AND INTOLERANCE

These seem to be increasing by the day. We may be turning into hypochondriacs – but maybe we're reacting to novel ingredients, or to the use of the same few products (fat, wheat, salt and sugar) in practically every food product on the market.

Benefits

None.

Dangers

Allergies can be fatal. Intolerance may cause a host of troublesome health conditions including irritable bowel syndrome and rashes.

Solutions

Individual: eat a wide range of foods and avoid any that cause bad reactions.

The big picture: the control of certain additives needed. More education about ingredients and processes.

PATENTING AND REGISTRATION OF PLANT VARIETIES

Though we can buy some exotic fruits that weren't seen here twenty years ago, the range of produce readily available to shoppers is actually much smaller. Thousands of old varieties of fruits and vegetables have disappeared. Most of those that we see in supermarkets now belong to a handful of multinational agrochemical companies.

Benefits
Huge profits for the agrochemical companies who own the seed patents.

Dangers
Loss of thousands of native plant varieties. Our choice of foods is narrowed down. From a health viewpoint, monocultures are always prone to disease and dependent on fertilisers and pesticides.

Solutions
Individual: if you're a gardener, join a seed club that distributes unusual varieties.

The big picture: campaign against further restrictions. Let shops know you'd like more variety.

WHAT YOU CAN DO

Ask the manager of your supermarket for the head office address, and write explaining your concerns. For example, say that you would like food to be labelled if it may contain genetically modified organisms. If they come back and say GM soy beans aren't separated from the rest of the crop, you could point out that it is not at all difficult to separate them, and you'd like the company to put pressure on manufacturers to ensure this.

Write to your MP. You can find out his or her name and

address from the House of Commons, on 0171-219 3000 or 0171-219 4272.

Joining a food safety group such as the Food Commission or the SAFE Alliance (see Resources) is easier and more encouraging than battling on alone.

RESOURCES

Anaphylaxis Campaign, 01252 318723.

Association of Breastfeeding Mothers, 0181-778 4769.
   PO Box 441, St Albans, Herts AL4 0AS.

British Airways travel clinics, tel 01276 685040.
   Contact for up-to-date information and the address of your nearest clinic.

British Allergy Foundation helpline 0171-600 6166/0891 516500.

Consumer's Association, 2 Marylebone Rd, London, NW1 4DF.
   Tel 0171-486 5544. Independent consumer watchdog, publishers of *Which?* magazine.

Examine your Own Food by RK Bahl, UK Consultancy Services, £17.50.

Food Commission, 94 White Lion Street, London N1 9PF, tel 0171 837 2250
   Independent consumer watchdog campaigning for food safety.

Food For Free by Richard Mabey, HarperCollins, £9.99

Food Labelling Agenda (FLAG) campaigns for all foods to be comprehensively and meaningfully labelled. PO Box 105, Hampton, Middlesex TW12 3TL. tel 0181-941 2977.

Foodline, 0800 282407, 14 Soho Square, London W1V 5FB. This free advice service is part of the Food Safety Advisory Centre, sponsored by supermarkets with an advisory panel of scientists and consumer advocates. Publication: *Food Safety Questions and Answers*, £1.99.

Travellers' Health: How to Stay Healthy Abroad by Dr Richard Dawood, Oxford University Press.

La Leche League (breastfeeding) PO Box BM 3424, WC1N 3XX, tel 0171-242 1278.

Malaria hotline, 0891 600350.

Medical Advisory Service for Travellers Abroad (MASTA),
    tel 0891 224100. Contact for up-to-date advice.
Mushrooms and Other Fungi of Great Britain and Europe by Roger Phillips,
    Pan Books, £13.99.
National Asthma Campaign helpline, 0345 010203.
National Childbirth Trust, 0181 992 8637.
National Society for Research into Allergy, PO Box 45, Hinckley,
    Leicestershire LE10 1JY, tel 01455 851546.
Secret Ingredients : The Essential Guide to What's Really in the Products you Buy
    by Peter Cox and Peggy Brusseau, Bantam, £6.99.
Soil Association, 86 Colston St, Bristol BS1 5BB,
    tel 0117 929 0661. Contact for information about organic food
    and links with food-safety groups and campaigns.
The SAFE Alliance, 38 Ebury Street, London, SW1W OLU,
    tel 0171 823 5660
Where to Buy Organic Food, The Soil Association (see above), £5
    including p&p.